The Open University

Volcanoes, earthquakes and tsunamis

David A. Rothery

Science Short Course

S186 Course Team

Chair and Author	David A. Rothery (Earth Sciences)
Critical Reader	Hazel Rymer
Course Managers	Isla McTaggart, Kat Hull
Editors	Amanda Smith, Peter Twomey
Media Developers	Greg Black (Interactive Media), Sara Hack (Graphic Artist), Chris Hough (Graphic Designer)
Media Project Manager	Rafael Hidalgo
Indexer	Jane Henley
Course Assessor	Professor W. J. McGuire, University College London

Cover Mount Fuji behind the Great Wave at Kanagawa; Japanese woodblock print by Katsushika Hokusai (1832).

The Open University
Walton Hall, Milton Keynes
MK7 6AA

First published 2007

Edited, designed and typeset by The Open University

Printed and bound in the United Kingdom by Halstan Printing Group, Amersham.

ISBN 978 0 7492 2678 7

1.1

Contents

Preface

So, you want to find out about volcanoes, earthquakes and tsunamis? These are closely linked in the popular imagination, and are the main hazards to life on our planet posed by the Earth's internal geological processes. In this course you will discover that volcanic eruptions and earthquakes are direct consequences of the way in which the outer layers of our planet are in continual motion. When a tsunami (sometimes erroneously called a 'tidal wave') happens, it is usually a result of either an earthquake or a volcanic eruption. In this course you will learn about: the causes of volcanic eruptions, earthquakes and tsunamis; what happens during these events; and what can be done to reduce the resulting fatalities and damage.

Erupting volcanoes constitute the most spectacular geological events that you can see happening, and you will encounter many examples during this course. The reach of volcanic eruptions is more extensive than that of earthquakes and tsunamis: the Earth's atmosphere owes its very existence to gases released by volcanoes in the distant past; the most extreme (and rare!) eruptions can cause global ecological disasters; and human societies have to learn to accept the long-term risks inherent in living on a volcanically active planet. I find volcanoes fascinating, and I am fortunate that I have been able to visit many volcanoes through my activities as a research scientist. Earthquakes and tsunamis can devastate whole regions (you will be aware of the tragic consequences of the very powerful earthquake on 26 December 2004 near Sumatra which triggered a tsunami affecting many coasts around the Indian Ocean) but at least their environmental impact is relatively short-lived.

This course will explain what causes volcanoes, and the ways in which they can erupt. It will then guide you through the types of volcano associated with different styles of eruption, the hazards posed by volcanic activity, and the ways in which volcanoes affect the climate. The course goes on to describe how scientists today seek to monitor and predict volcanic activity, and explores examples of both successful and unsuccessful management of volcanic crises. You will learn most of this by reading the Course Text *Teach Yourself Volcanoes, Earthquakes and Tsunamis* (abbreviated to TYVET). That is a book on sale to the general public, and this Study Book (the book you are reading now) will direct you to read sections (usually whole chapters) of it and then to return here, where you will find discussion and comment on the material in TYVET, additional illustrations and (very importantly in an Open University course) questions to help you test or develop your understanding and activities to help you develop skills or look at issues in greater depth (sometimes using material on the course DVD). Both are good practice for the End of Course Assessment, or ECA. As you study this course, earthquakes and tsunamis will crop up repeatedly among the volcanic phenomena that are dealt with first, and the final chapters complete the picture with a discussion of non-volcanic earthquakes and non-volcanic tsunamis.

You will also be introduced to the best internet sources of up-to-date information about volcanic activity, earthquakes and tsunamis – and you will learn how to explore these for yourself. By the end of this course you will have knowledge, understanding, experience and skills that will enable you to demonstrate achievement of the course's learning outcomes and should stand you in good stead if you decide to study other science courses.

All the course components and their functions are described in the S186 Study Guide. If you have not already done so, please read it now and then return to this Study Book to begin your study of the course.

Chapter 1 Introduction

Assuming that you are now ready (that is, you have read the Study Guide), it is almost time to look at Chapter 1 of *Teach Yourself Volcanoes, Earthquakes and Tsunamis* (TYVET), which is called simply 'Introduction'. This very short chapter sets the scene for the rest of the book. Note that the title page of this and every chapter in the book draws attention to the main things that you will learn from the chapter. This can be a useful pointer to what to look out for, but most chapters contain far more than can be fully summarised in this way.

You will learn best if you read 'actively' rather than 'passively': that is to say, *interact* with the text you are reading. To help you do this, you are advised to make a conscious effort to highlight important words or passages in TYVET, as suggested in Section 2 of the Study Guide. You can use either a highlighter pen to mark the key text or an ordinary pen or pencil to underline it. Doing this will force you to decide what you think is important, and will make it easier for you to refer back to these key passages later in your study. If you are unsure how to do this, wait until you have returned here where Activity 1.1 will help you to develop this aspect of active learning.

Read Chapter 1 of TYVET now. Note that there is a book symbol in the margin here to show you that you need TYVET at this point. It will be used in the same way throughout this Study Book. It is easy to spot the symbol, which is designed to make sure you have the right study materials to hand. Later in the course, you will see a symbol representing a DVD when you need to use the course DVD and a symbol representing internet access when you need to visit a website.

Return here when you have read Chapter 1 of TYVET.

1.1 Chapter 1 activity

If you were unsure which bits of Chapter 1 were worth highlighting, try doing Activity 1.1 before you read the discussion in Section 1.2. There are many activities in this course. Two of them, including Activity 1.1, need to use colour and are printed in this Study Book. For the others you will be directed at the right time to the Study Guide. It will generally take longer to do the activities than the questions, and you will need to work on some of them over an extended period. If a discussion is appropriate after you have finished, it will be near the end of the relevant book.

Activity 1.1 (overleaf) is a guide to which bits of TYVET pp. 2–4 it would be helpful to highlight. Even if you think your highlighting was adequate, look at the discussion to see whether your views coincide, and to note the recommendations about highlighting passages in this Study Book too.

It is not feasible to provide examples of highlighting text for all of TYVET. Instead, you will find that this Study Book includes at least one discussion section for each chapter. These sections draw attention to key points, but they also contain extra information and illustrations, and discussion of what you have read in the context of this course. The first of these discussions begins immediately below. Remember that you should highlight the key parts of this Study Book as well as

Activity 1.1 Highlighting key text

(The estimated time for this activity is 15 minutes.)

Page 2 of TYVET is the first page of standard text in the book. Unsurprisingly, the first three paragraphs of the chapter are of a general introductory nature. The third paragraph includes some personal reflections, which you might not have expected and need not be highlighted. However, there is some useful information in the previous two paragraphs that deserves to be picked out (Figure 1.1).

Figure 1.1
Example of highlighted text from the first two paragraphs of TYVET p. 2.

Volcanoes, earthquakes and tsunamis pose the most frightening 'geological' hazards that we inhabitants of planet Earth have to contend with. Probably, few people reading this book will be able to recall the occasion when they first heard the words 'volcano' and 'earthquake', because these are part of the common currency of everyday speech, imbued within us since early childhood. Even if you have never witnessed a volcanic eruption or experienced an earthquake, you probably have a clear (though not necessarily accurate) mental picture. On the other hand, the word 'tsunami' may be a much more recent acquisition to your vocabulary, acquired as a result of the tragic events of 26 December 2004 when a submarine earthquake near Sumatra displaced seawater into a devastating series of waves – a tsunami – that claimed nearly 300,000 lives around the shores of the Indian Ocean.

In this book, I try to help you understand the nature, causes and consequences of these natural phenomena. I begin by discussing the underlying mechanism whereby the Earth's surface is in motion and that causes both volcanoes and earthquakes, revealing why volcanoes and earthquakes tend to be concentrated into specific parts of the globe. I then look at how and why volcanoes erupt, and strategies to predict eruptions and to minimize the associated risk. Many famous cities lie beside volcanoes that have erupted in the past thousand or even the past hundred years, and that are certain to erupt again. For example, Auckland, the largest city in New Zealand, is built among a group of low-lying volcanoes whose most recent eruption was only eight hundred years ago. In the USA, parts of Seattle are on land liable to be devastated by mudflows that could be triggered by the next major eruption of Mount Rainier, only 35 km away. In Italy, Naples is built within range of Vesuvius, whose most recent eruption was in 1944 and which famously destroyed the Roman cities of Pompeii and Herculaneum in 79 AD.

The first paragraph gives an example of how a particular tsunami was generated. Here the phrases picked out are *submarine earthquake*, *displaced seawater*, *devastating series of waves* and *tsunami*. This links the cause (the earthquake), the mechanism (displacement of seawater) and the effect (a series of waves); it also reveals that a tsunami is a *series* of waves rather than just one wave. Clearly, much more could be said (and will be, later in the book), but you have already gathered some significant information here.

In the second paragraph, the highlighted words show that the book will discuss the *underlying mechanism* that *causes both volcanoes and earthquakes*, and pick out examples of famous cities and their volcanoes.

With this example of highlighting in mind, now reread the rest of Chapter 1 (TYVET pp. 3 and 4), and highlight important phrases or words as you do so (the final paragraph draws your attention to the Glossary of specialist terms, so you need not highlight anything there). When you have done this, compare what you have done with the suggestions in the discussion of this activity near the end of this book.

TYVET. There is space here to write notes in the margin, to comment on the text. This is done for you in Section 1.2, as an example, but after that it is up to you.

1.2 Discussion of Chapter 1

Even though this is a short chapter, a few points are worth noting. First, volcanoes and earthquakes are each manifestations of the Earth's mobility (this is discussed in Chapter 2), whereas tsunamis are a phenomenon that can be triggered by a volcanic eruption, by an earthquake, or by an unrelated mechanism, according to the circumstances.

Relationship between volc, eq and tsn

Second, Auckland (Figure 1.2a), Seattle and Naples (Figure 1.2b) are cited as examples of cities close to volcanoes described as 'certain to erupt again'. It is very important to realise that this is an entirely different prospect to the buried (and ancient) volcanic rocks below many parts of the world, and the 340 million-year-old volcanic rocks exposed at the surface in and around Edinburgh (Figure 1.2c) or the even older rocks of the English Lake District (Figure 1.2d). Some volcanoes only ever erupt once, most remain active for up to a few hundreds of thousands of years, and a few rather special ones can be active for maybe 2 or 3 million years (for comparison, Earth is known to

(a) (b)

(c) (d)

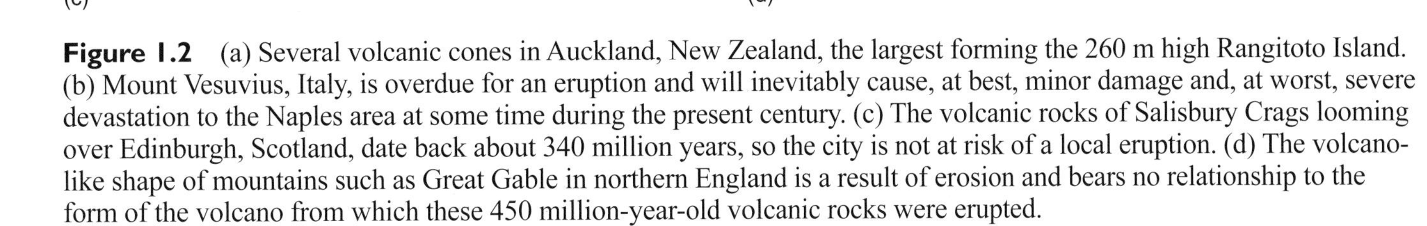
Figure 1.2 (a) Several volcanic cones in Auckland, New Zealand, the largest forming the 260 m high Rangitoto Island. (b) Mount Vesuvius, Italy, is overdue for an eruption and will inevitably cause, at best, minor damage and, at worst, severe devastation to the Naples area at some time during the present century. (c) The volcanic rocks of Salisbury Crags looming over Edinburgh, Scotland, date back about 340 million years, so the city is not at risk of a local eruption. (d) The volcano-like shape of mountains such as Great Gable in northern England is a result of erosion and bears no relationship to the form of the volcano from which these 450 million-year-old volcanic rocks were erupted.

Different significance of modern and ancient volcanoes

be about 4550 million years old). On the other hand, a volcano old enough to be buried or dating back more than 10 million years no longer poses any risk of an eruption.

It is far from simple to decide whether you as an individual or the global community as a whole should be more concerned about the risks posed by volcanoes, by earthquakes, or by tsunamis. To some extent it depends on the timescale that you are prepared to consider. For example, taking the long-term view, it is not a very useful statistic that, during the 20th century, earthquakes claimed far more lives than volcanic eruptions. Globally devastating eruptions are fortunately very rare (there has not been one in historic times) but, averaged over a hundred thousand years, you may expect more deaths from eruptions than from earthquakes. This theme is considered further later.

Remember to check Glossary at end of TYVET!

The final paragraph reassures you that you should be able to make sense of TYVET even if geology (or geoscience in general) is not yet familiar to you, but explains why technical terms are sometimes necessary. It also reassures you that such specialist terms are explained and identified in **bold** type where they first appear, and points out that they are also explained in a Glossary on TYVET pp. 280–9.

1.3 Chapter 1 questions

At the end of (and sometimes within) the discussion for each chapter, you will find a few questions (such as those below) which are intended to help you satisfy yourself that you have understood the main points covered in the chapter and the commentary on it here. You will find answers and, where appropriate, discussion of them at the end of this Study Book. You are strongly recommended to attempt to answer the questions for yourself *before* looking at my answers because they are good practice for your ECA. However, you must not feel that it is 'cheating' if you need to refer back to information and discussion in any of the course materials to help you. The ability to locate and extract relevant information from various sources is a skill that is valued by most scientists and an important one to develop as a student.

Chapter 1 is fairly basic, so the questions on it are not very challenging. Some of the questions on later chapters are less straightforward.

Answers and comments for all the numbered questions are given near the end of this book.

Question 1.1

For how long can a volcano remain active?

Question 1.2

Which one of the following cities is not at risk of a local volcanic eruption, and why?

(a) Auckland

(b) Naples

(c) Edinburgh

(d) Seattle

Question 1.3

How did the famous eruption of Krakatau in 1883 kill most of its victims?

Chapter 2
How the Earth moves

When you have read this paragraph, you should start studying TYVET Chapter 2, remembering to highlight what you judge to be the key parts of the text as you go along. (If you find it difficult to judge, looking ahead to the questions in this Study Book will identify at least some of them for you.) This chapter is a much more serious proposition than Chapter 1. Furthermore, if you are unfamiliar with geoscience, you may find it harder going than any of the later chapters, because it deals with the basic structure and composition of the Earth, and describes rather strange melting processes. This is necessary background information for the discussion of volcanoes in Chapters 3 and 4. Please persevere and remember that the discussion in this Study Book is intended to explain or clarify any issues that have confused you in TYVET. You will meet earthquakes at several places in this chapter, and discover that volcanoes and earthquakes are both consequences of Earth being a geologically active planet. Don't read right to the end of Chapter 2: when you reach the section 'Plate tectonics, earthquakes and magma generation' on p. 13, return to this Study Book.

2.1 Discussion of Chapter 2, pp. 5–13

The start of Chapter 2 may have surprised you by stating that the Earth's interior is largely *not* molten (for reasons that begin to be explained on p. 11). It does at least reassure you that the Earth's interior is hot, although it does not specify the temperature, which is about 1200 °C near the top of the mantle and probably in the region of 5000 °C in the inner core.

The section 'Magma and minerals' introduces the term 'magma', which geologists use to denote molten rock, and the term 'igneous' to refer to any rock that was formerly molten. It introduces the term 'mineral', which denotes the crystals that form as a molten rock cools. Box 2.1 gives some background on minerals.

TYVET then introduces the term 'basalt', which geologists use to denote a particular variety of igneous rock. You will meet a few other such names later in Chapter 2. Many of these names will become familiar if you study geology, but few are important in this course.

The next two sections – 'Compositional layering of the Earth's interior' and 'Mechanical layering of the Earth's interior' – tell you how the Earth's internal structure can be divided into concentric zones according to either composition or mechanical properties. In some places the two coincide: for example, the boundary between the lower mantle and the outer core juxtaposes solid rocky material (silicate minerals) over a liquid mixture of iron and (probably) sulfur. The compositional difference between the crust and the mantle is much less radical than the mantle–core difference, and both are solid. However, the crust and the uppermost mantle form a single *mechanical* layer, which behaves in a strong and rigid fashion and is called the 'lithosphere', while the deeper mantle is weaker and is, in fact, in a state of (very slow) internal flow. TYVET points out that the slow flow of the deeper mantle does *not* mean that it is liquid. You may find this a surprising concept because it is a material property not often encountered on everyday timescales. However, consider

Box 2.1 Minerals

It is not straightforward to define what is meant by the term 'mineral'. A simple statement such as 'a mineral is a naturally occurring crystalline substance with a well defined chemical composition' is a good starting point. However, this is too restrictive to be an adequate definition because, although the arrangement of atoms within the crystalline structure of any particular mineral is fixed, the overall chemical composition may vary (by substitution of one element for another). On the other hand, some minerals that are regarded as distinct from each other share the same arrangement of atoms, and are distinguished by differences in their chemical composition (which may radically affect their colour or other properties). Some minerals have an *identical* chemical composition but the atoms are arranged differently, giving the crystals totally different properties (these are called 'polymorphs'). A few substances of non-crystalline form are usually regarded as minerals too.

A thorough investigation of a mineral would require chemical analysis, study of its optical properties using a microscope, and X-ray analysis of its atomic structure. However, a common mineral occurring as a crystal bigger than a few millimetres long often shows enough clues for a moderately experienced geologist to make a fairly confident identification. There are several features to look out for, including: lustre (does it look metallic or glassy?); colour (but impurities can make this misleading); cleavage (planes of weakness within the atomic structure of the crystal, manifested by tiny planar fractures); general shape (related to cleavage in some, but not all, minerals); and hardness (how easily can it be scratched?).

Minerals can sometimes grow as large and beautifully formed crystals (Figure 2.1) but in volcanic rocks the crystals are usually too small to be easily visible.

Figure 2.1 Some examples of large crystals of minerals which are common, as much smaller crystals, in volcanic rock. Each image is a few centimetres across. (a) Quartz, (b) olivine, (c) feldspar, (d) pyroxene, (e) amphibole.

a block of pitch at room temperature (or the toy material called 'silly putty' at fridge temperature). If you were to hit this with a hammer, you could shatter it and you would be in no doubt that it was solid. On the other hand, if you were to leave it alone for a few weeks, it would slowly lose its shape and begin to spread out; thus it is a solid capable of flow over a long time-period. Most of the Earth's mantle behaves like this, except that flow is driven by contrasts in buoyancy between the warmer mantle below and the cooler mantle above, which stimulate the convection described on TYVET p. 12.

TYVET Figures 2.1 and 2.2 show the important aspects of the Earth's compositional and mechanical structure, which are summarised here in Figure 2.2. You may have found it difficult to understand some of the diagrams. If so, Box 2.2 gives some advice on getting the most out of diagrams.

Figures in TYVET and in this Study Book have the same numbering convention. To make it clear which one is meant, a figure called 'Figure X.X' means a figure in this book and a figure called 'TYVET Figure X.X' means a figure in the Course Text. The same convention is used to distinguish tables.

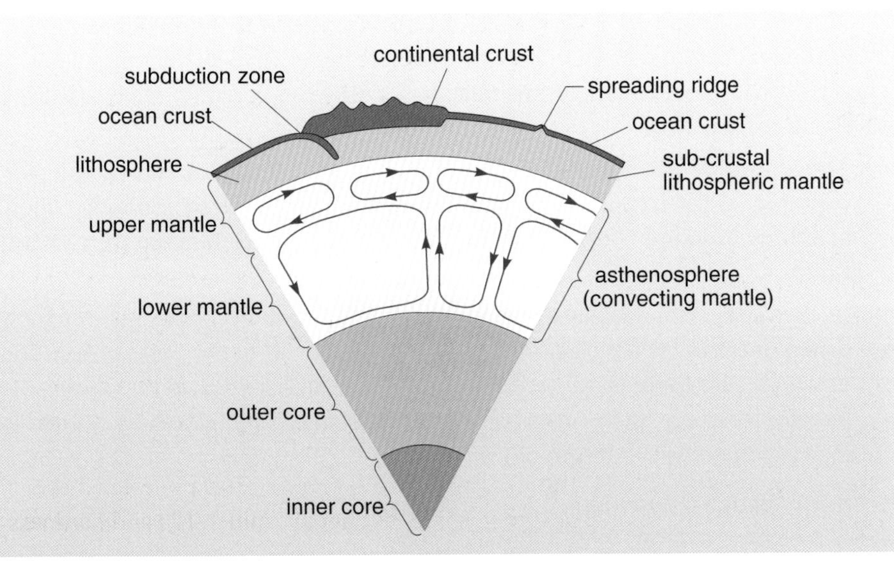

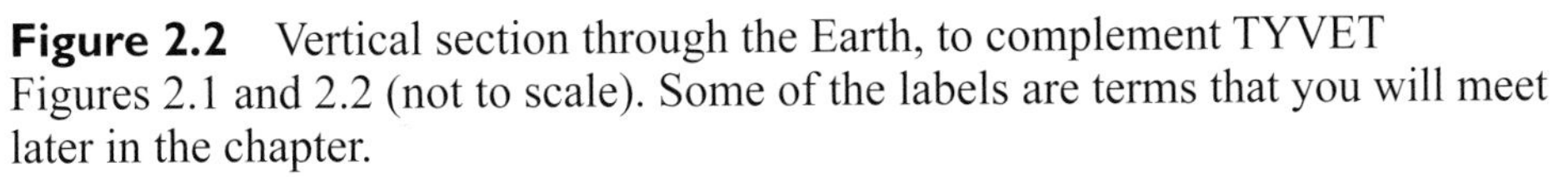

Figure 2.2 Vertical section through the Earth, to complement TYVET Figures 2.1 and 2.2 (not to scale). Some of the labels are terms that you will meet later in the chapter.

Box 2.2 Studying diagrams

When you meet a new diagram, you need to study three aspects. First, read the caption, which tells you what the diagram is about. Second, quickly look at the diagram to get an overall impression and, third, work through all the labels, checking the parts to which they relate. In this course you will meet several different sorts of diagram and you will be given advice on how to read and interpret them. Don't worry if the initial impression is complicated; working through a diagram step by step will enable you to understand its meaning.

Earthquakes are referred to several times in this part of TYVET, but the term is not defined. Two simple definitions of 'earthquake' taken from the internet, which are sufficient for now, are:

> The sudden motion or shaking of the ground produced by abrupt displacement of rock masses.
>
> Shaking of the Earth caused by a sudden movement of rock beneath its surface or from volcanic activity.

Note that sudden movement of rock (such as that associated with an earthquake) within the Earth tends to be confined to the lithosphere, because this is the strong, rigid layer. In contrast, if any process distorts the weaker asthenosphere, this layer can deform gradually and continuously, without the kind of sudden rupture necessary to cause an earthquake. You will learn more about the motion of the lithosphere and asthenosphere in the rest of Chapter 2.

The 'Oxide' column of TYVET Table 2.1 shows chemical formulae, using the conventional chemical abbreviations for the elements. This is the only place where you will meet chemical formulae in TYVET, so you only need to know the following information.

- The abbreviations for many elements make perfect sense in English: for example, O for oxygen, Si for silicon and Ti for titanium. Others – such as Fe for iron and Na for sodium – derive from other languages, chiefly Latin.
- In chemical formulae, subscript numbers indicate the proportions in which different elements are combined (unless they are all in the same proportion, in which case there is no need). For example, SiO_2 indicates two atoms of oxygen for every atom of silicon; Al_2O_3 indicates three atoms of oxygen for every two atoms of aluminium.

If you are feeling overwhelmed by the strange new words that you have met, Box 2.3 has suggestions which may help you.

Box 2.3 A personal glossary

In TYVET most of the specialist terms appear together in its Glossary (pp. 280–9). However, you may find it helpful to create a 'personal glossary' of your own definitions. This has two main advantages. First, the process of choosing which words to include from each part of the course helps you identify the important points. Second, thinking about definitions and writing them in your own words will help you remember them better. There are several ways of laying out such a personal glossary. In choosing what suits you, please bear the following points in mind.

- Your glossary will be easiest to use if it is arranged, at least approximately, alphabetically.
- You don't know in advance how many terms there will be.
- You may want your glossary to be 'portable', so that you can have it with you wherever you are studying.

It could be in the form of:

- a small notebook, which you can divide by the letter of the alphabet
- an address book, or similar, already divided by letter
- a loose-leaf binder, with a page for each letter, to which more can be added if needed
- file cards in a small box
- a database on your computer.

There is a trade-off between, on the one hand, perfect alphabetical order and ease of searching (in which the computer wins easily) and, on the other hand, convenience (a small notebook is best). It is probably wise not to spend time setting up a very elaborate system at first, until you are sure that you will use it. Think of the compilation of your personal glossary as an ongoing activity during the course.

Now try to answer the following questions, to test whether you have grasped the main points of the first part of Chapter 2 and, if not, to help consolidate your understanding.

Question 2.1

What are the differences between melt, magma and lava?

Question 2.2

Which contains the highest proportion of silica: continental crust, oceanic crust or the mantle?

Question 2.3

(a) Which of the Earth's compositional layers make up the lithosphere?

(b) How does the lithosphere differ from what lies below it?

(c) What name does TYVET give to the junction between crust and mantle?

2.2 Studying the rest of Chapter 2

On TYVET p. 11 you read that the lithosphere consists of several independent slabs or 'plates', which move around as described by the theory of 'plate tectonics'. The rest of the chapter describes plate tectonics in more detail, and shows how it leads to the generation of magma that feeds volcanoes. Stresses built up during the movement of tectonic plates also cause earthquakes of the kind sometimes called 'tectonic' to distinguish them from those caused by volcanic processes.

Read the rest of Chapter 2 now, not forgetting to highlight where you think this will help you. While you read, you should make a few notes on each of the three ways in which plate tectonics brings about the process of 'partial melting' because you will need this to answer Question 2.4. Return here when you reach the end of the chapter.

2.3 Discussion of Chapter 2, pp. 13–26

This discussion begins with the question you were asked to work on while reading this part of TYVET.

Question 2.4

TYVET describes three ways in which plate tectonics causes partial melting. Write a *one-sentence* description of each one that includes an explanation of why partial melting happens in that particular case.

This part of TYVET provides only a small and highly simplified map of the Earth's plate boundaries in TYVET Figure 2.4. You may find the alternative version here (Figure 2.3) clearer. Figure 2.4 shows a three-dimensional cross-section from South America to Africa, combining elements of TYVET Figures 2.5 and 2.6.

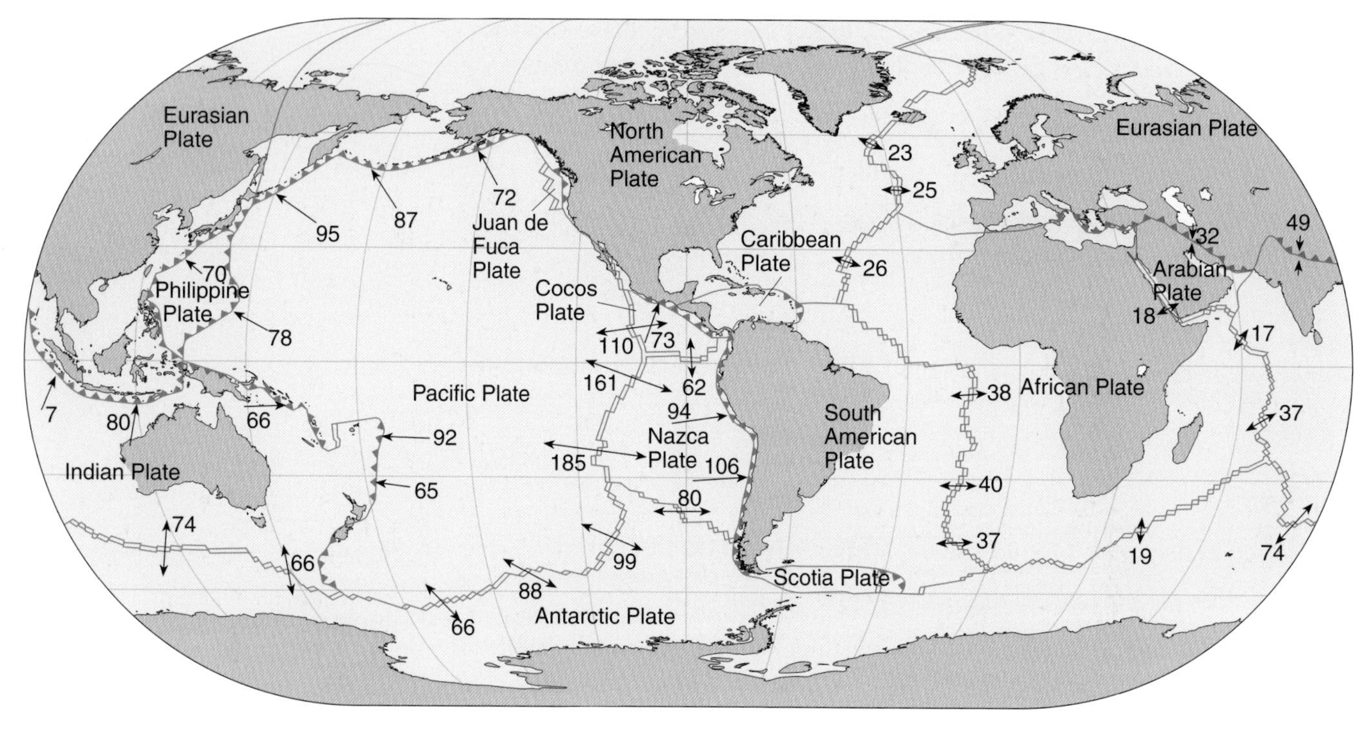

Figure 2.3 Map of the global distribution of plates and plate boundaries. The black arrows and numbers give the direction and speed of relative motion between plates, with speeds in millimetres per year. (This is a different convention from TYVET Figure 2.4, where the rates are expressed relative to Earth as a whole.)

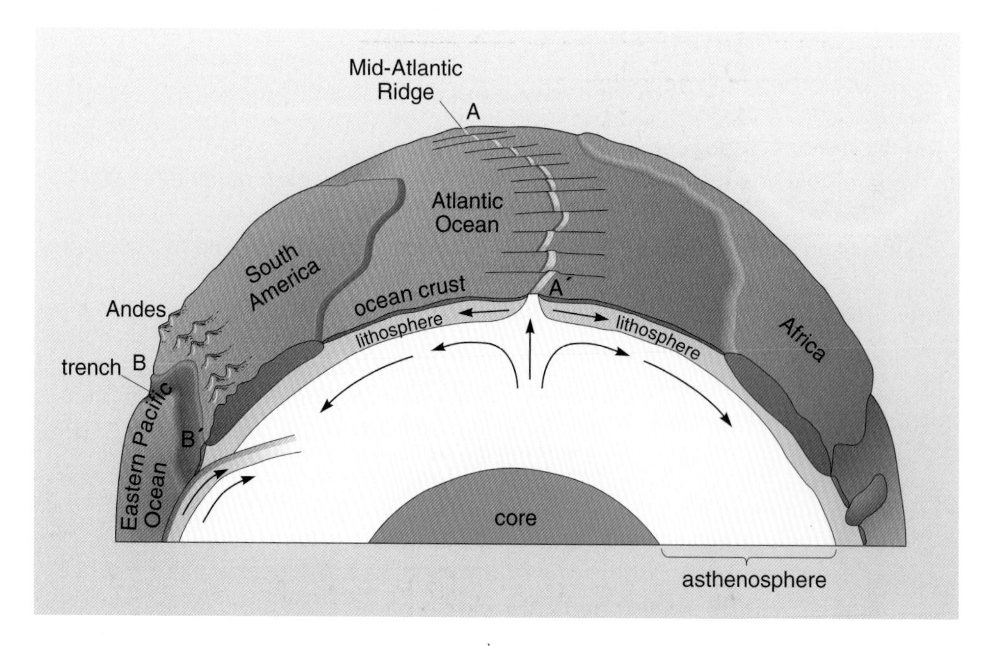

Figure 2.4 Vertically exaggerated, cut-away view of Earth to show the plate tectonic relationships between three tectonic plates: the African plate, the South American plate, and the plate forming the floor of the Pacific Ocean to the west of South America. The Earth's lithospheric plates are moving apart at constructive plate boundaries (such as A–A′) where new material is continually added to the diverging edges of the plates, but are converging across destructive plate boundaries (such as B–B′) where the descending (subducting) plate is eventually absorbed into the deep mantle.

This is an example of a 'stop and think' type question. Unlike the numbered questions, these do not require you to write down an answer. However, you will benefit by trying to work one out *before* you read my answer.

■ In Figure 2.3 one of the three types of plate boundary is given a different name to that used in TYVET Figure 2.4. Which one?

□ Conservative plate boundaries are marked as transform fault plate boundaries, using the term 'transform fault' which you met in TYVET. (Elsewhere you may find constructive plate boundaries described as 'divergent' plate boundaries and destructive plate boundaries described as 'convergent' plate boundaries.)

In the third paragraph of the section 'Plates colliding' there is a comment that is particularly relevant in a course that deals with earthquakes as well as volcanoes, which is that motion between two masses of rock in the lithosphere 'does not happen uniformly, but progresses in a series of occasional jerks that give rise to earthquakes'. This jerky motion is known as 'stick–slip' and you will learn more about it in Chapter 9. A fracture in the lithosphere that allows motion between two masses of rock is called a 'fault'. The plate boundaries mapped in Figure 2.3 and TYVET Figure 2.4 are the largest faults on the planet. TYVET Figure 2.6 illustrates how the sources of earthquakes (labelled 'earthquake focus') are used to map how steeply a subducting plate dips below the overriding plate. All types of plate boundary are closely associated with earthquakes (Figure 2.5). You will study this relationship in more detail in Chapter 9.

These figures plus the text in TYVET should tell you all you need to know about the general mechanics of plate tectonics but the relationship of plate motions to magma generation merits further elaboration.

The most important point about magma generation is that it does not happen as a result of *complete* melting of the source material (with the rare exceptions noted at the end of the chapter). This is because the Earth's interior consists of a mixture of different minerals and, in such mixtures, each mineral will begin to melt at a different temperature. Thus the melt becomes enriched in silica and elements such as sodium, potassium, calcium, aluminium and iron, whereas the unmelted residue in the source becomes correspondingly depleted in these ingredients. This is called 'partial melting'.

The composition of magma depends on the plate tectonic setting where it is generated. The only source of melt at a constructive plate boundary is the mantle, which has the composition called 'peridotite'. Partial melt extracted from peridotite will be slightly richer in silica (and certain other ingredients) and so will have the composition of the rock type called 'basalt'. Source regions for partial melting at destructive plate boundaries are much more varied, and hence give rise to magmas of all compositions ranging from basalt, through andesite to rhyolite. In Chapter 4 you will read that magma composition can evolve further during its rise towards the surface.

This part of TYVET also describes how most volcanoes are related to plate tectonics. Volcanoes are particularly associated with destructive plate boundaries, in the form of Andes-type mountain belts (where oceanic lithosphere is subducted below a continent), or island arcs (where subduction occurs below the oceanic part of a plate). There are two general exceptions to the usual spatial relationship between volcanoes and plate boundaries. 'Hot spot' volcanoes occur above deep-seated, pipe-like upwellings from the deep mantle called 'mantle plumes', and are fed by magma generated by decompression melting. Plate movements are independent of these plumes, so hot spot volcanoes can occur anywhere

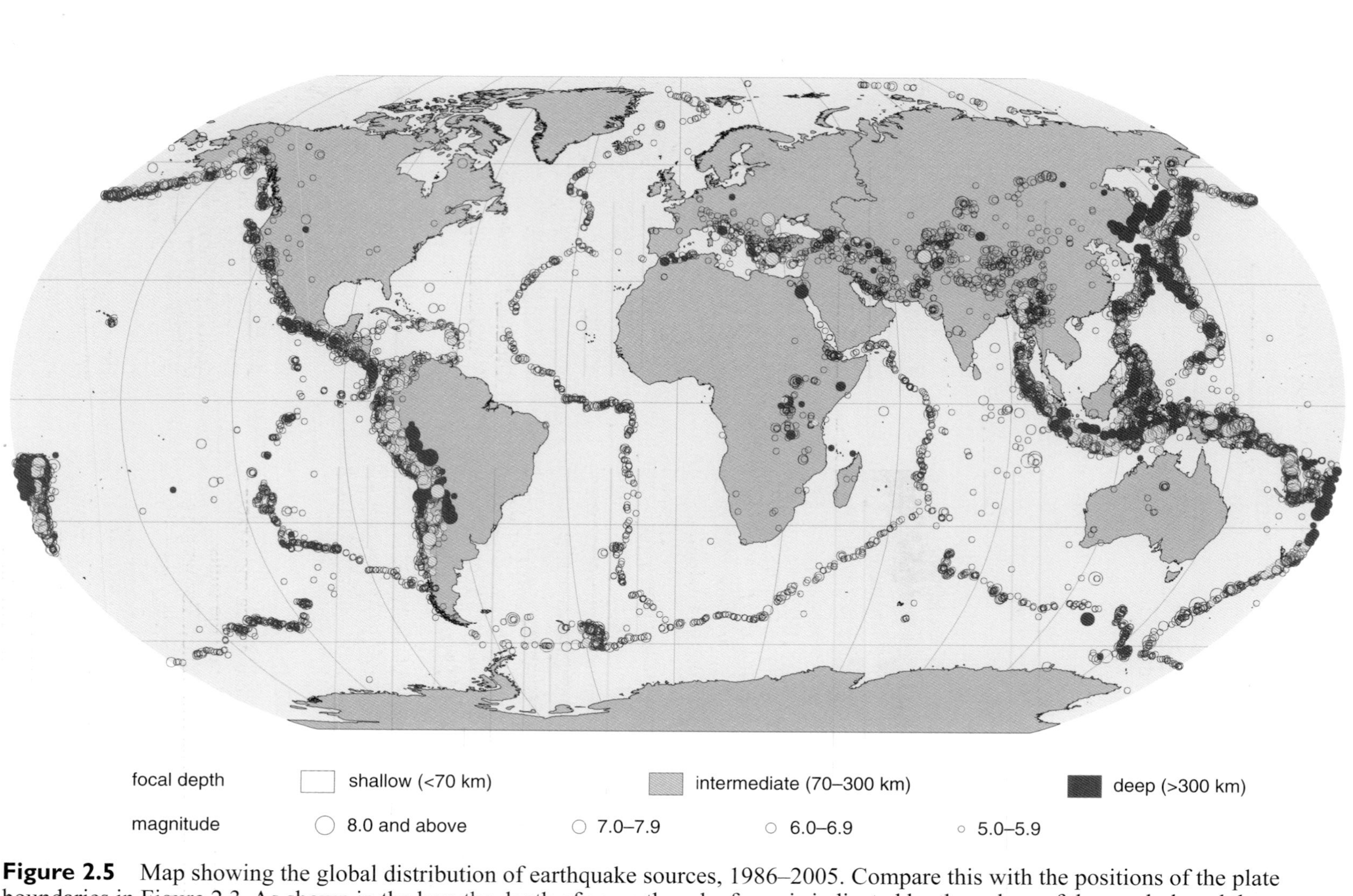

Figure 2.5 Map showing the global distribution of earthquake sources, 1986–2005. Compare this with the positions of the plate boundaries in Figure 2.3. As shown in the key, the depth of an earthquake focus is indicated by the colour of the symbol, and the magnitude (defined in Chapter 9) by the size of the symbol.

around the globe; Hawaii is the best-known example. The other exception does have a link to plate tectonics, in that it happens along zones of weakness where a continental plate may be in the process of beginning to rift apart but has not yet split into separate plates. The volcanoes of the East African Rift (Figure 2.6) are the classic example.

Finally, the clarity of some of the black-and-white landscape photographs in TYVET is rather poor, so colour versions are often shown here, such as Figure 2.7. There are also pictures such as Figure 2.8, which were left out of TYVET because there was not enough space.

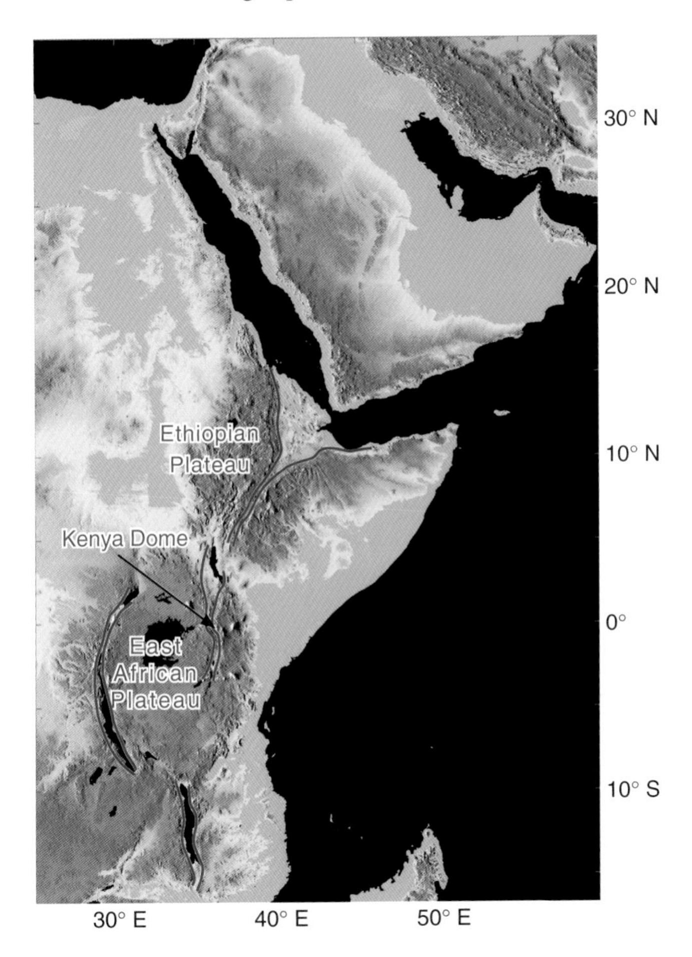

Figure 2.6 Map of eastern Africa and Arabia with red lines added to indicate the faults bounding the African Rift Valley. Topography is colour-coded, ranging from green (less than 1 km) to yellow (1–2 km), brown (2–3 km) and grey (more than 3 km). Most individual volcanoes are too small to show up at this scale, but Mount Kilimanjaro, a volcano which is the highest peak in Africa, is visible on the east side of the rift (level with the word 'African').

Figure 2.7 The edge of the African Rift Valley in Ethiopia (colour version of TYVET Figure 2.12).

Figure 2.8 Dubbi, a 160 m high volcano which last erupted in about 1900. This volcano is in Eritrea where the African Rift Valley widens near to the Red Sea, in a setting equivalent to that in TYVET Figure 2.11.

Now try to answer the following questions, to help consolidate your understanding and to test whether you have grasped the main points of this part of Chapter 2.

Question 2.5

According to Figure 2.3 and TYVET Figure 2.4, what is the name of the plate labelled 'Eastern Pacific Ocean' in Figure 2.4 in this Study Book?

Question 2.6

In which direction would you expect earthquakes to get deeper at the destructive plate boundary between the Nazca Plate and the South American Plate, and why?

Question 2.7

At which type of plate boundary do volcanoes typically *not* occur, and why?

2.4 Chapter 2 activities

Did you highlight the text in TYVET as you worked through it? I won't keep going on about it, but most students find that highlighting helps both their initial study and their subsequent revisiting of the text. Please do Activity 2.1 now, which is a final attempt to convince you!

Activity 2.1 More highlighting

(The estimated time for this activity is 15 minutes.)

Chapter 2 (and all the following chapters) has much more information worth highlighting than Chapter 1. If you have not already done so, please now highlight the key elements of the section 'Plates moving apart' (TYVET pp. 14–15), and then compare what you have done with the suggestions in the discussion of this activity.

Activity 2.2 Dynamic Planet interactive map

(The estimated time for this activity is 30 minutes.)

There are detailed notes for this activity in the Study Guide. The internet symbol in the margin means that you need access to the internet to do the activity.

Chapter 3 Eruptions

Chapter 3 introduces you to volcanic eruptions. 'Eruption' is the term used by volcanologists (volcano scientists) to denote the arrival of volcanic products at the Earth's surface. To reach the description of the wide range of ways in which an eruption can manifest itself, you first have to read about what causes magma (generated by partial melting) to rise towards the surface, and how this magma may change during its ascent. Then you will learn about the 'plumbing' systems beneath volcanoes, before getting to grips with the variety of ways in which an eruption can occur. The chapter also considers what can trigger an eruption, how eruptions are measured, and whether or not volcanologists can tell that a volcano has definitely finished erupting for ever. As you read, highlight key phrases to pick out concepts that strike you as important. This will make them stand out, and make them easier to find whenever you want to refer back to them. There are probably several concepts that will be new to you.

Now read TYVET Chapter 3 to the end of the section 'How rising magma evolves' (p. 36). While you read, make notes on the ways in which the composition of a rising batch of magma can change. You will need this information to answer Question 3.2.

3.1 Discussion of Chapter 3, pp. 27–36

The section 'Magma migration and magma rise' describes how magma must gather into a sufficiently large mass if it is to rise fast enough ever to reach the surface. Deep fissures can provide convenient pathways for rising magma to follow, but time is still required for magma to squeeze out slowly from between crystals in order to take advantage of any open pathways. You are told that magma is typically *less dense* than the surrounding rock. Magma therefore has a tendency to rise, because the pressure within the Earth acts to push it upwards. You are also introduced to the concept of *viscosity*. A liquid with a low viscosity flows relatively freely, whereas a liquid with a high viscosity flows sluggishly (it may help you to think of 'viscosity' as the inverse of 'fluidity'). It will make your understanding of volcanic processes easier if you can remember that the higher the silica content of magma, the higher its viscosity.

This section of TYVET also describes how magma is often stored below volcanoes in magma chambers, where some magma becomes completely solidified and is never erupted. You read that this forms what is called 'plutonic igneous rock'. Geologists can study plutonic rock only because of erosion of the Earth's surface, which in mountain belts can cut down at a rate of 1 cm or more per century. Erosion can thus take less than a hundred million years to expose an intrusion that was formed at a depth of 10 km.

Question 3.1

Try to work out this time for erosion for yourself, given an erosion rate of 1 cm per century.

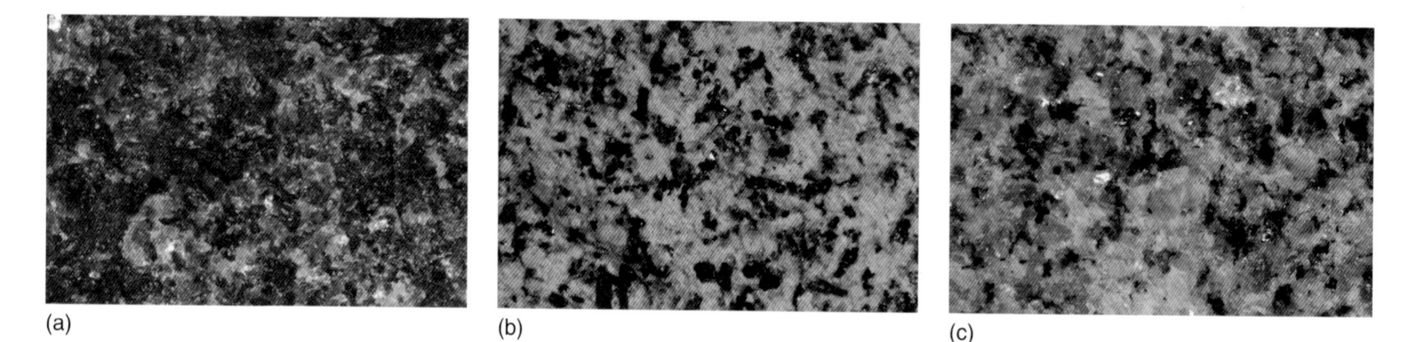

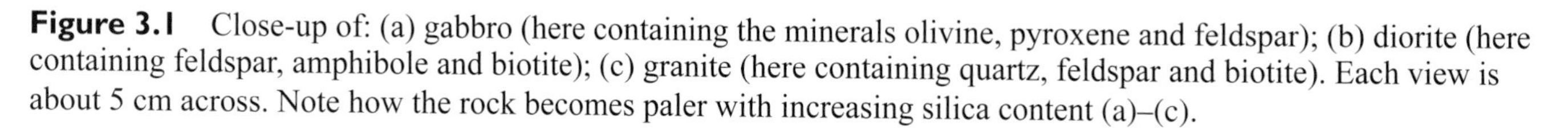

Figure 3.1 Close-up of: (a) gabbro (here containing the minerals olivine, pyroxene and feldspar); (b) diorite (here containing feldspar, amphibole and biotite); (c) granite (here containing quartz, feldspar and biotite). Each view is about 5 cm across. Note how the rock becomes paler with increasing silica content (a)–(c).

The text names gabbro, diorite and granite as coarse-grained plutonic rocks of differing silica content, and TYVET Figure 3.2 shows a close-up of a piece of diorite. Figure 3.1 here shows colour photographs of all three rock types.

The section 'How rising magma evolves' describes several ways in which the composition of a rising batch of magma can change. Answer Question 3.2 to check whether you have understood them.

Question 3.2

List the ways in which the composition of a rising batch of magma can change, and write *one or two sentences* describing each process, noting changes in the melt or magma composition in each case.

Volatiles (either dissolved in magma or escaping as gas) play a crucial role in determining the nature of volcanic eruptions, as described later in the chapter.

3.2 Studying the rest of Chapter 3

Now read the rest of Chapter 3 to the end. Don't worry if the scientific convention for expressing large numbers used in TYVET Table 3.1 is unfamiliar to you – it is explained below in Box 3.1.

3.3 Discussion of Chapter 3, pp. 36–64

The section 'Volcano plumbing' discusses the fissures and pipe-like channels through which magma can migrate towards the surface. The six types of feature named in TYVET Figure 3.8 will become familiar as you study the course. The most curiously named one is 'shallow magma chamber', which denotes a volume within the crust occupied by magma. It would be wrong to think of a magma chamber as being an otherwise empty space simply waiting for magma to arrive. Except possibly in the upper few hundred metres of a volcano, magma chambers expand or contract according to the volume of magma present, and are unlikely ever to contain a large 'empty' (or gas-filled) void.

Figures 3.2 and 3.3 are colour versions of TYVET Figures 3.6 and 3.7, showing more clearly the gas escaping from these two volcanoes. In both cases, the gas plume is made visible because water vapour condenses to form tiny suspended droplets (as in an ordinary cloud). Figure 3.4 shows colour versions of the views in TYVET Figure 3.11.

Figure 3.2 A prominent gas plume escaping from a vent on Masaya volcano in Nicaragua (colour version of TYVET Figure 3.6).

Figure 3.3 Telica volcano in Nicaragua: note the faint haze of gas escaping from the crater, which is hard to see in TYVET Figure 3.7.

Figure 3.4 (a) San Pedro volcano in Chile and (b) the satellite cone that has built up at the site of a secondary vent (colour versions of TYVET Figure 3.11).

You also met the term 'seismometer' for the first time. On volcanoes, seismometers are instruments used to detect and measure vibrations caused by volcanic activity. You will learn more about them mainly in Chapter 7. As you will see in Chapter 9, seismometers are also used to detect and measure vibrations travelling away from sites of tectonic earthquakes.

The section 'Eruptions' is long and contains subsections on 'Pyroclastic eruptions' and 'Lava flows and lava domes'. These divide volcanic products into those produced by violent fragmentation (pyroclastic) and those produced by extrusion.

Pyroclastic eruptions are usually a consequence of explosive fragmentation of the magma as it erupts, but they can also be caused by the collapse of solid material. You will learn much more about the nature and consequences of such eruptions in later chapters. Plinian eruptions (TYVET p. 47) are especially important because they can be particularly devastating. You will learn much more about these as you progress through the course. Figure 3.5 shows a close-up view of a plinian airfall deposit.

Figure 3.5 Cross-section through a plinian airfall deposit, here consisting largely of centimetre-sized lumps of pumice. The coin near the centre gives the scale (close-up view of the plinian deposit shown in TYVET Plate 8).

As you should have gathered, lava flows themselves can break into lumps of various sizes, but these are usually bigger than a brick, which distinguishes them from violently fragmented pyroclastic material, the majority of which is much finer grained. The two Hawaiian terms used to describe the morphology of basalt lava flows are a'a (pronounced 'ah-ah') and pahoehoe (pronounced either 'pa-hoey-hoey' or 'pa-hoy-hoy'). Figure 3.6 shows these two varieties side-by-side. In Activity 3.1 there is video of moving images of lava flows for you to watch, which should clarify many of the processes described in the text.

Figure 3.6 Colour version of the lower image in TYVET Figure 3.24, showing a'a lava (left) partially overridden by a subsequent pahoehoe flow (right).

There are two crucial ways in which the escape of volatiles from solution in the magma influences eruptions. First, the growth of bubbles makes the magma (including its bubble content) less dense than before. This increases the buoyancy of the magma, so it will tend to rise faster than before. Second, the growth and expansion of bubbles can force magma out of a conduit explosively, giving rise to explosive pyroclastic eruptions. An eruption is likely to be effusive only when any volatiles can escape quietly (which is easiest from low-viscosity magma).

You will encounter the VEI (the Volcanic Explosivity Index) many times during this course. It is used as a basis for comparing the sizes of explosive eruptions. Box 3.1 (overleaf) explains the number convention used in the definition of this scale.

Question 3.3

According to TYVET Table 3.1, what volume of fragmental material must be erupted for an eruption to be classified as VEI 8? (Express your answer in plain English.)

Question 3.4

Write a brief account, *in about 100 words*, of the factors that control the height of an eruption column. Include page references to your sources of information.

Each of the four final sections of Chapter 3 is relatively brief. 'Eruption triggers' considers what events can set off an eruption. It also draws your attention to the difference between tectonic earthquakes and volcanogenic earthquakes. Tectonic earthquakes, which are symptoms of plate-tectonic movements, occasionally trigger a volcanic eruption. On the other hand, earth tremors associated with

Box 3.1 The VEI scale and understanding powers of ten

The middle column of TYVET Table 3.1 (p. 51) expresses values in a way that is conventional in science. If you have studied science before, perhaps this table holds no mysteries for you (in which case, you can ignore this box). Otherwise, there are just four facts that you need to know.

1 The column heading shows that it classifies the volume of fragmental material erupted in units called 'm^3'. The 'm' is straightforward – it is simply the standard abbreviation for 'metres' (just as 'km' in the third column means 'kilometres'). However, the ^{3} might have perplexed you. In fact, 'm^3' means '$m \times m \times m$', which is a measure of volume. You can say 'm^3' as 'metres cubed' or 'cubic metres'.

2 The volumes are expressed as ranges using 'powers of ten'. For example, to have a VEI rating of 3 the volume of fragmental erupted material has to be more than 10^7 m^3 but less than 10^8 m^3. '10^7' means 1 followed by 7 noughts, which is 10 000 000 (ten million), whereas 10^8 means 1 followed by 8 noughts, which is 100 000 000 (one hundred million). You can say '10^7' as 'ten to the power seven' or 'ten to the seven', and '10^8' as 'ten to the eight', and so on.

3 There are two other special symbols: $<$ means 'less than'; $>$ means 'more than'.

4 Except for VEI 0 and 1, each increase of one unit on the VEI scale corresponds to a *tenfold* increase in erupted material. A scale arranged like this is especially useful for reporting anything that covers a range spanning many powers of ten. Elsewhere, you may find that scales such as this are referred to as *logarithmic*.

If you are still confused, or want to know more, please refer to Sections 7 and 8 in the Maths Skills ebook.

magma movement (that is, volcanogenic earthquakes) are ubiquitous consequences of volcanic activity. As you will learn in Chapter 7, monitoring volcanogenic earthquakes is probably the single most effective means of predicting eruptions.

'The sizes of eruptions' introduces the concept of eruption *magnitude*, which is similar to VEI except that it can be applied to all types of eruption rather than just explosive ones, and eruption *intensity*, which quantifies the rate at which material is erupted.

'Eruption frequency and duration' may have surprised you in revealing that as many as 60 volcanoes erupt in an average year. It also showed that eruptions of VEI 6 and greater are much rarer than smaller ones. Few of the latter usually receive much attention from the world's news media. This section also tells you how long an eruption can last, and the duration of the active lifetimes of the most persistent volcanoes. However, what some observers report as a series of eruptions could be regarded by different observers as phases of a single, drawn-out eruption. Part of the reason for this confusing situation is there is often a period of doubt at the end of an eruption about whether it has finished or merely paused.

Finally, 'Non-erupting volcanoes' introduces volcanoes that are active without erupting and explains what volcanologists mean by the terms 'dormant' and 'extinct' (see the TYVET Glossary for a definition of these terms).

Now do Activity 3.1, and then try to answer Questions 3.5–3.12 to consolidate your understanding of what you have learned during your study of this chapter.

Activity 3.1 'Lava flows' video

(The estimated time for this activity is 40 minutes.)

The notes for this activity are in the Study Guide. The DVD symbol in the margin is a flag to you that you need the course DVD at this point.

Please refer to the discussion of this activity in the Study Guide before attempting the questions in Section 3.4. In the video there were several glimpses into active lava tubes through holes in the roof described as 'skylights'. A view of a skylight is shown here in Figure 3.7.

If you don't believe what was said in the video about frying eggs on pahoehoe lava, Figure 3.8 proves that it can be done.

(a) (b)

Figure 3.7 A skylight above a lava tube feeding a pahoehoe field on Kilauea, Hawaii in 2000: (a) volcanologists deploying instruments to record the temperatures within the skylight; (b) view into the skylight from the instrument array.

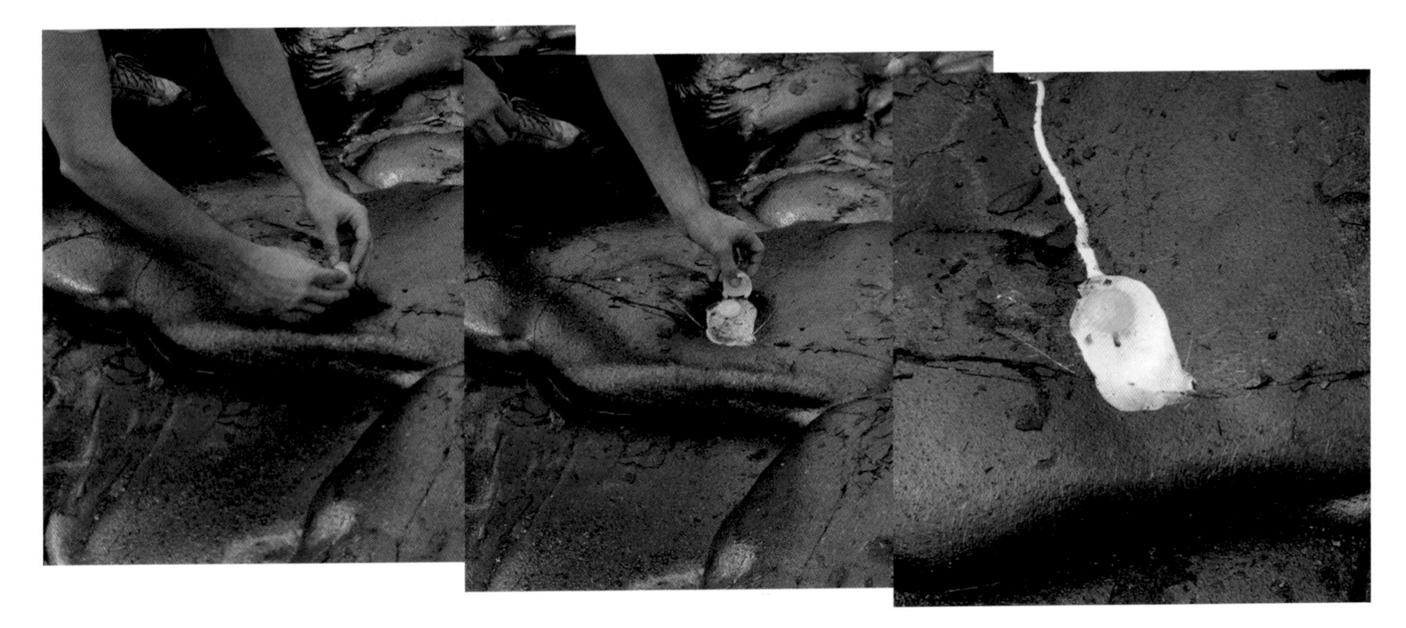

Figure 3.8 Frying an egg on a 10-minute-old lobe of pahoehoe.

3.4 Chapter 3 questions

Now try to answer the following questions to consolidate your understanding and to test whether you have grasped the main points of this part of this chapter. Question 3.5 relates specifically to Activity 3.1, and the other questions relate to Chapter 3 as a whole.

Question 3.5

According to the 'Lava flows' video (Activity 3.1), how does lava reach an eruptive fissure?

Question 3.6

(a) According to TYVET, how many VEI 6 eruptions would you expect there to be, somewhere in the world, during an average century?

(b) What is the likelihood of there being a VEI 7 eruption in your remaining lifetime? (Express this as a numerical probability if you can.)

Question 3.7

What is the effect of dissolved volatiles on the viscosity of silicate magma?

Question 3.8

What kind of *effusive* eruption on land can lead to the creation of a pyroclastic deposit, and how is the pyroclastic deposit generated?

Question 3.9

Place the following types of magma in order of increasing viscosity: andesite, basalt, carbonatite, rhyolite.

Question 3.10

In two or three sentences each, describe (a) the similarities and (b) the differences between plinian and vulcanian eruptions.

Question 3.11

What are the two main factors in determining the nature (surface texture) of a basalt lava flow? Briefly describe the effect of each factor.

Question 3.12

Write the terms 'volcanic eruptions' plus either 'volcanogenic earthquakes' or 'tectonic earthquakes' in either of the blank spaces in the statements below, to make as many correct statements as you can.

___ always trigger ___.

___ sometimes trigger ___.

___ never trigger ___.

Chapter 4
Types of volcano

Now study Chapter 4, in which you will learn about the landscape features produced by different kinds of eruption. The text is fairly descriptive, building on your understanding of processes introduced in Chapters 2 and 3. *Before* you begin, write down a definition of the word 'volcano', to compare with your increased understanding of the term when you reach the end of the chapter. There is not a specific task to do while you read this chapter (although highlighting and adding to your personal glossary will help you engage more with the text). You should read to the end of the chapter before you return here.

4.1 Discussion of Chapter 4

Did you realise that you have studied the first three chapters of the Course Text without being told (or even invited to consider) what a volcano is? Maybe you thought you knew already, so it didn't occur to you to define this fundamental term until you were asked to try it. You should not be surprised (or ashamed) if the definition you wrote before you read Chapter 4 now seems rather inadequate. The first three paragraphs of the chapter argue that it makes sense to avoid being trapped by too narrow a definition. By the time you reached the end of the chapter, you should have realised that some volcanoes barely resemble any kind of mountain.

The section 'Composite cone volcanoes' discusses the kind of mountain that the word 'volcano' conjures up in most people's imagination. These certainly form breathtakingly beautiful landscape features, as demonstrated by the photographs in TYVET and Figure 4.1 here. Figure 4.2 shows the sloping layers of airfall material and lava flows responsible for both the name and the shape of composite cone volcanoes.

(a) (b)

Figure 4.1 (a) Acamarachi, a composite cone volcano reaching an altitude of over 6000 m in northern Chile. Its most recent eruption was several thousand years ago. (b) Lastarria, a composite cone volcano reaching an altitude of 5697 m on the border between northern Chile and Argentina. Its most recent eruption was probably only a few hundred years ago. In the foreground there is a blocky andesitic lava flow. The yellow ground high on the flank is sulfur deposited at fumaroles, from which white clouds of steam are emerging.

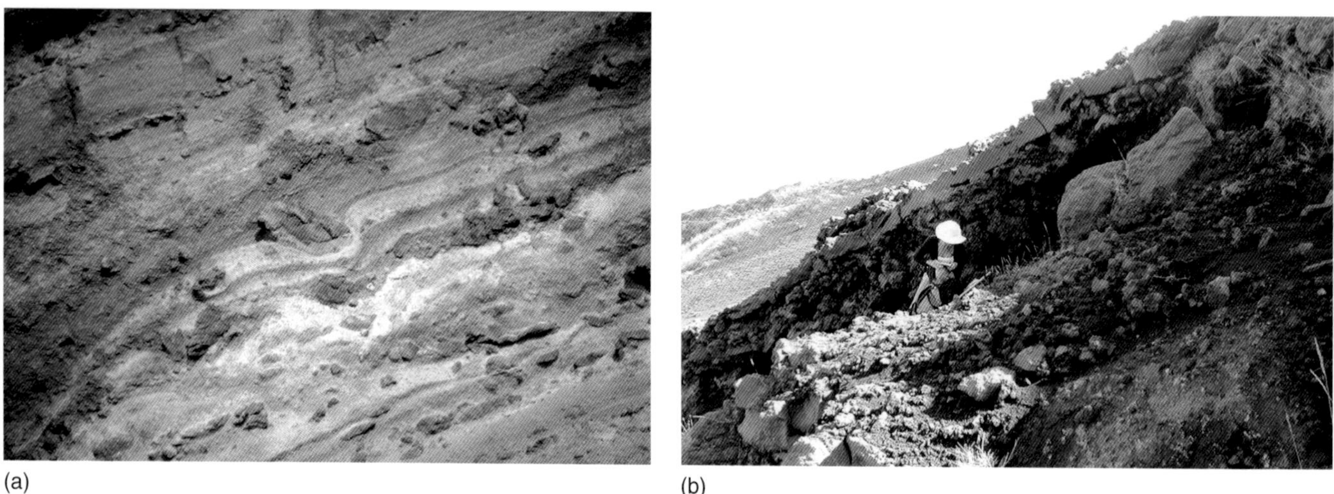

(a) (b)

Figure 4.2 Stromboli volcano, Italy. (a) Section through layers of ash and coarser airfall. The cliff face shown is about 8 m high, and the largest bomb visible (near the centre) is nearly 2 m long. (b) Lava flow (above the woman's head) overlying a coarse, bomb-rich airfall deposit (immediately behind her).

Not all composite cone volcanoes (not even all of the active ones!) have symmetrical cone shapes though, as you should have discovered.

■ What two reasons are given in TYVET to explain why some composite cone volcanoes have non-symmetrical shapes?

□ One reason is that the location of the conduit can change over time, and this migration of the vent results in the volcano growing as a ridge rather than as a cone. Another reason is that part of a volcano can collapse; this destroys part of the mountain, while distributing a debris avalanche across the adjacent terrain.

You will learn about the hazards posed by collapsing volcanoes in Chapter 5. Meanwhile, you may be interested to know that the lava dome formed within Mount St Helen's collapse amphitheatre is still growing, despite an 18-year pause between October 1986 and October 2004 (TYVET Figure 4.10 and Figure 4.3 here).

The next section was about shield volcanoes, which are built by eruptions of basalt lava. An important message in this section is that basaltic shields can range from huge (Figure 4.4a) to relatively small (Figure 4.4b).

TYVET mentions that the Galápagos Islands are made of shield volcanoes, but it does not illustrate or discuss them. The typical profile of Galápagos shields differs from that of Hawaiian shields; Galápagos shields tend to have flatter summits (with deeper calderas) but steeper flanks (Figure 4.5). Like Hawaii, the Galápagos Islands owe their existence to being situated above a mantle plume, but Galápagos shields are smaller. There are more of them and nine have erupted in historic times. No one is sure why the sizes and shapes here are different from Hawaii, but it may relate to differences in the thickness of the local lithosphere, the vigour of the mantle plume, and the rate of plate movement over the plume.

(a) (b)

Figure 4.3 Mount St Helens in Washington State, USA. (a) A view across Spirit Lake before the 18 May 1980 eruption. (b) Slightly closer view across the same lake in 1982. The steaming lava dome can be glimpsed within the collapse amphitheatre. In the foreground, trees that were stripped of their branches and uprooted by the directed blast are floating in the lake.

(a) (b)

Figure 4.4 (a) Mauna Loa in Hawaii, seen from the opposite side to that in TYVET Figure 4.15. This is a giant shield volcano, built up by eruptions over tens of thousands of years. (b) Mauna Ulu on the flanks of Kilauea in Hawaii. This was created in a single series of eruptions from 1969 to 1974, and measures about 1 km across its base.

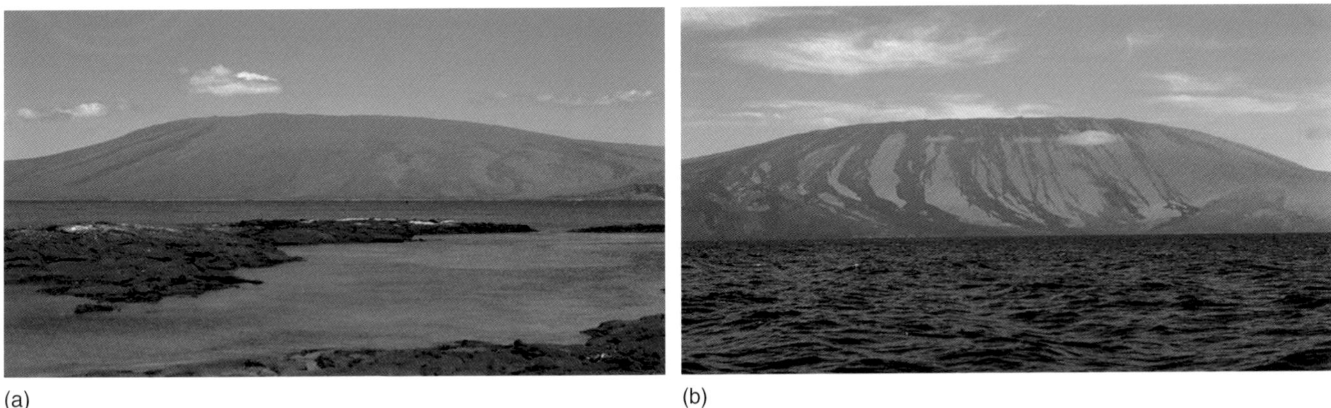

(a) (b)

Figure 4.5 Volcanoes (a) Darwin and (b) Wolf in the Galápagos Islands. Note the relatively steep flanks, compared with Hawaiian shields, giving these volcanoes a profile reminiscent of an inverted soup bowl.

The section 'Flood basalts' deals with the products of the largest-volume eruptions on Earth. Two are illustrated here in Figures 4.6 and 4.7. In Chapter 4 you read how flood basalts are rare but represent vast outpourings of basalt lava in a geologically short timescale, although the rate of emplacement of each individual flow within a flood basalt remains controversial. You will learn about the global environmental effects of flood basalt eruptions in Chapter 6.

Figure 4.6 (a) The extent of the Deccan Traps flood basalt province in India. These 64–67 million-year-old lavas reach a maximum thickness of 2.5 km to the east of Mumbai. (b) Panoramic view showing about 1 km thickness of lava flows near Mahabaleshwar.

Figure 4.7 Columbia River flood basalts, USA. (a) The extent of the province which erupted mostly 14–17 million years ago. The deep purple area maps a single flow (the Pomona flow), which can be traced 550 km from its source. (b) Cross-section through more than a dozen individual flows exposed on a hillside.

It is interesting to compare the volume of a flood basalt province with the volume of material erupted by a VEI 8 eruption. Box 4.1 shows you how to do this.

Box 4.1 Comparing erupted volumes (more about powers of ten)

According to TYVET Table 4.1 (p. 85), the volume of lava in a flood basalt province is about one million cubic kilometres. If you turn back to Table 3.1 (p. 51), you will find that a VEI 8 eruption ejects $>10^{12}$ m^3. If this is called 10^{13} m^3, to represent a huge VEI 8 eruption, is this more, or less, than the volume erupted in a flood basalt province?

The comparison is a little tricky because TYVET quotes flood basalts in (millions of) cubic kilometres but uses cubic metres for the VEI scale. Before making a comparison, you must get both measurements into the same units. The simplest way to do this is to turn cubic metres into cubic kilometres.

■ There are 1000 (or 10^3) metres in a kilometre, so how many cubic metres are there in a cubic kilometre?

□ $1\ km^3 = 1000\ m \times 1000\ m \times 1000\ m$, or $10^3\ m \times 10^3\ m \times 10^3\ m = 10^9\ m^3$. In other words, $10^9\ m^3 = 1\ km^3$

■ So, how many cubic kilometres are represented by the 10^{13} cubic metre VEI 8 eruption?

□ The answer to this is $(10^{13}/10^9)\ km^3$, which is $10^{13-9}\ km^3$, which is $10^4\ km^3$ or 10 000 km^3.

If you don't know this rule about subtracting powers of ten when you want to divide one by another, try to remember it, because it is handy when doing sums with large numbers. (Similarly, if you need to multiply two numbers that are expressed as powers of ten, you just *add* the powers.)

So, you have worked out that the VEI 8 eruption is about $10^4\ km^3$. A flood basalt province is about one million km^3, which is $10^6\ km^3$. This is clearly bigger than the $10^4\ km^3$ VEI 8 eruption. To find out how much bigger, just divide one by the other: $10^6\ km^3/10^4\ km^3 = 10^{6-4} = 10^2 = 100$.

So, the volume of a flood basalt province is about a hundred times the volume erupted in an extreme VEI eruption.

In fact, the 100-fold difference in volume is rather an underestimate for two reasons. First, flood basalt lavas are dense and solid, whereas the products of explosive VEI 8 eruptions are low-density ash and pumice. This means that the volume of magma erupted in an explosive eruption is less (by a factor of two or three) than the volume of the deposit. Second, the largest flood basalt eruptions are *several* million cubic kilometres, rather than just one million cubic kilometres. The difference in magma volume between a large VEI 8 eruption and a large flood basalt province is thus more like one thousand than one hundred.

The next section brings you right back to the bottom of the size-and-volume scale of volcanic edifices – monogenetic features. If you are ever fortunate enough to

Figure 4.8 Scoria cones on Mount Etna in Sicily, Italy (colour version of TYVET Figure 4.24).

visit any young volcanic features, monogenetic features are good because they are relatively small and so easier to explore than most other volcanoes. Furthermore, being monogenetic, there is almost no risk of being caught in an unexpected eruption, which cannot be said of visiting other volcanoes. Figures 4.8–4.11 show colour views of some monogenetic features, to supplement those in TYVET.

- ■ Is there anything particular about the colour of the inside rim of the nearer of the two scoria cones in Figure 4.8?

- □ It is faintly red. The scoria here has reacted with volcanic gases or rainwater while still hot, and some of the iron in minerals such as pyroxene has been oxidised and hydrated to form what is effectively rust.

(a) (b)

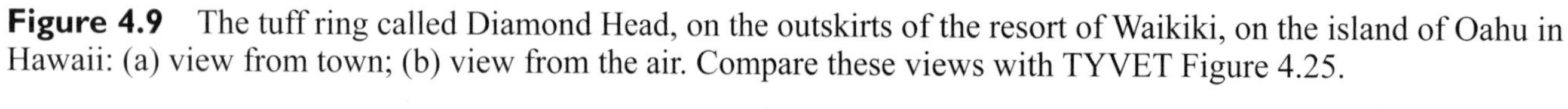

Figure 4.9 The tuff ring called Diamond Head, on the outskirts of the resort of Waikiki, on the island of Oahu in Hawaii: (a) view from town; (b) view from the air. Compare these views with TYVET Figure 4.25.

(a) (b)

Figure 4.10 East Ukinrek Maar in Alaska: (a) aerial view in 1994; (b) aerial view showing the column of ash and steam generated by the eruption that created the maar in 1977.

Figure 4.11 The tuff cone called Koko Crater on Oahu in Hawaii. (a) View from the side opposite to that in TYVET Figure 4.26. (b) The layers of ash from which the cone is built, exposed by marine erosion. This view is looking roughly towards the centre of the cone, so the layers are sloping towards the camera and dip more steeply than is apparent in this view. The white lumps are chunks of coral ripped off the sea floor during the explosive mixing of magma and seawater below the vent.

The section 'Calderas' introduces the kind of volcano produced when a large explosive eruption (or a series of them) takes place, usually involving magma relatively rich in silica. Caldera-forming eruptions can completely destroy a composite cone volcano, and are the largest eruptions to have occurred during human history. You will learn about the impact that such eruptions can have on the global climate in Chapter 6.

Figure 4.12a shows the famous caldera of Crater Lake in Oregon, USA. This is clearer than the version shown in TYVET. Figure 4.12b shows a poorly known caldera on the mainland of Antarctica called Mount Hampton, which was discovered during an airborne survey in 1940. Other calderas are so big that they can be properly recognised only from space. For example, Cerro Galan (Figure 4.13) in a remote part of northwest Argentina was not recognised as a caldera until the late 1970s.

Figure 4.12 (a) Crater Lake, a 9 km diameter caldera in Oregon, USA (colour version of TYVET Figure 4.30). (b) Mount Hampton in Antarctica, an ice-filled caldera 6 km across, the highest part of the rim being 3325 m above sea level.

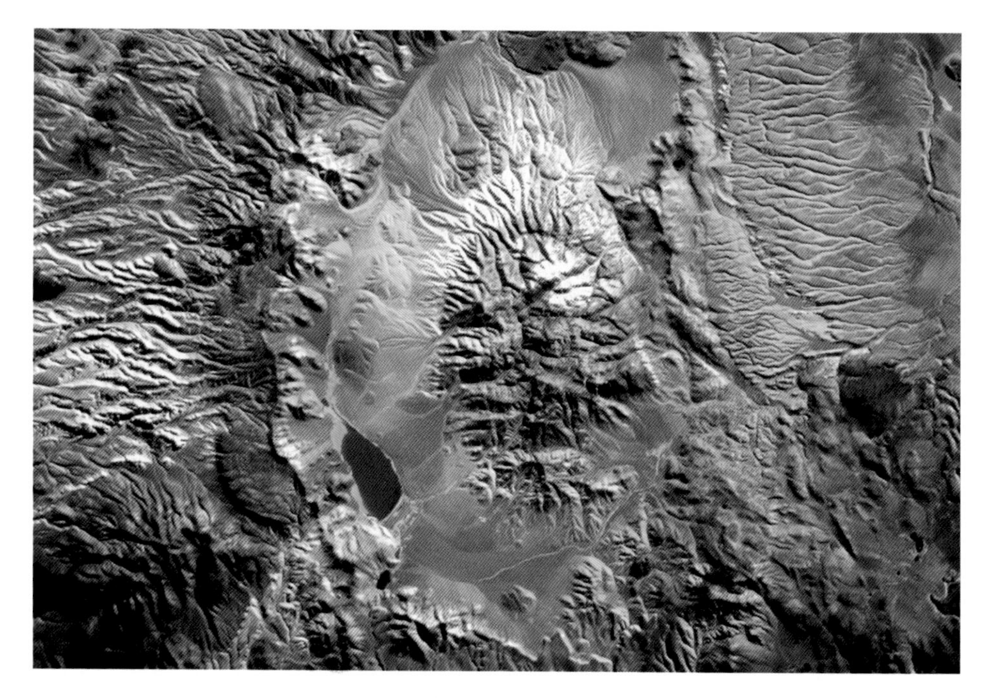

Figure 4.13 Cerro Galan in Argentina, a caldera measuring 35 km (north-south) × 25 km (east-west), from a satellite image (colour version of TYVET Figure 4.32).

The section 'Subglacial volcanoes' is about volcanoes that erupted below an ice cap rather than volcanoes that happen to be beneath an ice cap today. These will not be considered further in this course, although in Chapter 5 you will read a little about the special kind of hazard posed when they erupt. The final section, 'Undersea volcanoes', deals with volcanoes that are far more widespread.

■ In which plate-tectonic setting would you expect most undersea volcanoes to occur?

□ At constructive plate boundaries, where new crust is continually being built by volcanic processes.

TYVET Figure 4.34 shows a perspective view of the bathymetry (underwater topography) of part of a constructive plate boundary. This is repeated in colour in Figure 4.14a. Undersea volcanoes range in size from simple mounds of pillow lava (too small to show up in Figure 4.14a), which are the equivalent of monogenetic features on land, to full-scale 'seamounts'. The seamounts in Figure 4.14a are sufficiently close to the plate boundary that one of them could erupt again. However, those in Figure 4.14b are about 18 million years old, and are certainly extinct. They are in line because they were created one after another by locally intense magma supply at a now vanished hot spot on a constructive plate boundary. This is in contrast to the seamount chain that has Hawaii at its active end, where the hot spot occurs within a plate rather than at a plate boundary.

In Figure 4.14b note the evidence for the formation of successive calderas in the most northwesterly seamount, followed by sector collapse to produce a debris avalanche deposit extending towards the neighbouring seamount. The most southeasterly seamount has experienced a more limited collapse.

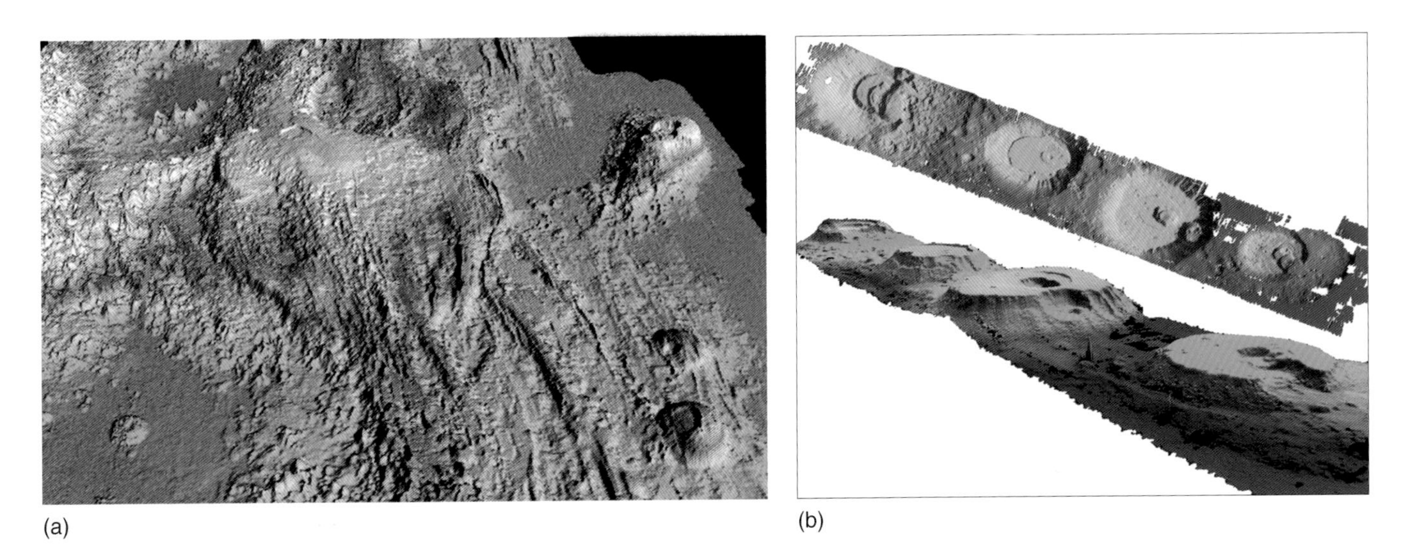

Figure 4.14 (a) Juan de Fuca Ridge in the northeast Pacific Ocean. Bathymetry has been colour-coded on this perspective view (colour version of TYVET Figure 4.34). (b) Taney seamount chain, which is 100 km long and about 300 km west of San Francisco, on the floor of the Pacific Ocean: above, map view (north at top); below, perspective view, vertically exaggerated by a factor of two. Bathymetry has been colour-coded (blue representing the deepest), but the range of colours is different in the two examples.

On human timescales, it is rare for an active submarine volcano to emerge above sea level. It seems that the lava dome that grew on Metis Shoal in Tonga in 1995 still survives. You may find it listed on the internet as the 'youngest island in the world', the second youngest being claimed to be the island of Fukutoku-Okanoba, which emerged near the Japanese island of Iwo Jima in 1986. However, the tuff cone built by the Fukutoku-Okanoba eruption in 1986 was destroyed by wave action within two months, although submarine eruptions continued until about 1997. On the other hand, the volcano Home Reef, only 20 km from Metis Shoal, which appeared briefly above sea level in 1984, was erupting again and had emerged in the form of a tuff cone while this course was being prepared in 2006. These are all in island-arc settings, where the general water depth is much shallower than is typical near mid-ocean ridges. If a new volcanic island erupts while you are studying this course, you will certainly know about it via the course website. Meanwhile, Figure 4.15 shows a rather beautiful painting of the eruption of Graham Island in the Mediterranean in 1831.

Figure 4.15 Activity on the short-lived volcanic island known as Graham Island to the British and Ferdinandea to the Italians. New material is pictured being added to the island from either a (continuous) fire fountain or a (intermittent) strombolian eruption (colour version of TYVET Figure 4.36).

Now do Activities 4.1 and 4.2 and then answer Questions 4.1–4.3, to conclude your study associated with this chapter.

Activity 4.1 The Global Volcanism Program website

(The estimated time for this activity is 30 minutes.)

The notes for this activity are in the Study Guide.

Activity 4.2 'Eruption styles' video

(The estimated time for this activity is 30 minutes.)

The notes for this activity are in the Study Guide.

4.2 Chapter 4 questions

Now try to answer the following questions, to help consolidate your understanding and test whether you have grasped the main points of this chapter.

Question 4.1

What do Mount St Helens, Tenerife and the Hawaiian Islands have in common?

Question 4.2

Why are basaltic shield volcanoes less steep than composite cone volcanoes?

Question 4.3

Rank the following monogenetic volcanic features in order of *increasing* water content during eruption: tuff cone, tuff ring, scoria cone.

Question 4.4

You were asked to write a definition of 'volcano' before you began to study this chapter. How would you define the term now you have reached the end of the chapter, and how has your definition changed?

Chapter 5
Volcanic hazards

Now read Chapter 5, which discusses the various hazards posed by volcanic eruptions, illustrated by examples from recent eruptions. Make sure you have watched the 'Eruption styles' video (Activity 4.2) before you begin. While you read Chapter 5 and do the activities afterwards, it would be a good idea to compile your own table of hazards, with as many examples of each one as you can find. This will be useful for answering some of the questions at the end of the chapter and maybe in the ECA. This table simply needs two columns: one headed 'Hazards' and the other headed 'Examples'. For each example, be sure to include a page reference to TYVET (later you can add references to the Study Guide or the websites visited in the activities); this will be convenient in case you need to inspect the original information again. You will meet the term 'micrometre' in connection with the size of very tiny ash particles; a micrometre is one-millionth of a metre, which is one-thousandth of a millimetre. Return here when you reach the end of the chapter.

5.1 Discussion of Chapter 5

Were you surprised by the wide variety of ways in which volcanic eruptions can cause death and destruction? If you were, ask a friend or a family member to name a volcanic hazard: they will probably say 'lava'. (Try it! It can help you to improve your understanding if you talk to people about your studies.) However, having read this chapter, you should realise that lava flows are a comparatively minor problem in most cases. Although, except in the rare case of a successful diversion attempt, immovable property is destroyed by lava (Figures 5.1 and 5.2), people have to be particularly unfortunate (or stupid) to be killed by a lava flow. You will see a hazardous lava flow in Activity 5.1.

Pyroclastic flows are much more dangerous. You have seen these in Activity 4.2, and Figure 5.3 shows a clearer view than the photographs in TYVET.

(a) (b) (c)

Figure 5.1 Burial of a store in Kalapana, Hawai, between (a) April and (b and c) June 1990 (colour versions of TYVET Figure 5.1).

Figure 5.2 A burning house in Kalapana, Hawaii, surrounded by a thin sheet of pahoehoe in 1990.

(a) (b)

Figure 5.3 (a) The deadly pyroclastic flow on Montserrat in the Caribbean, 25 June 1997 (another view of the event in TYVET Figure 5.8). (b) The thin deposit left by the pyroclastic flow in (a).

At the time of writing, the most recent VEI 6 eruption is that of Mount Pinatubo in the Philippines in 1991 (Figure 5.4), notable for a plinian eruption column, 35 km high, which led to a heavy airfall as well as column-collapse pyroclastic flows. You will learn how the build-up to this eruption was monitored and how the crisis was managed in Chapter 7.

The threat posed to aircraft by volcanic ash clouds is another matter and is considered further in Chapter 7. However, it is worth emphasising here that the disposition of ash clouds and the airfall that is deposited below them are controlled by the wind direction(s) during the eruption. Figure 5.5 maps the pattern of airfall distribution from the 18 May 1980 eruption of Mount St Helens showing clearly the effect of wind blowing from the west. Please see Box 5.1 (on p. 37) for an explanation of the contoured information on maps such as Figure 5.5.

Figure 5.4 The VEI 6 plinian eruption of Mount Pinatubo in the Philippines, 12 June 1991 (a slightly different view from TYVET Figure 5.11).

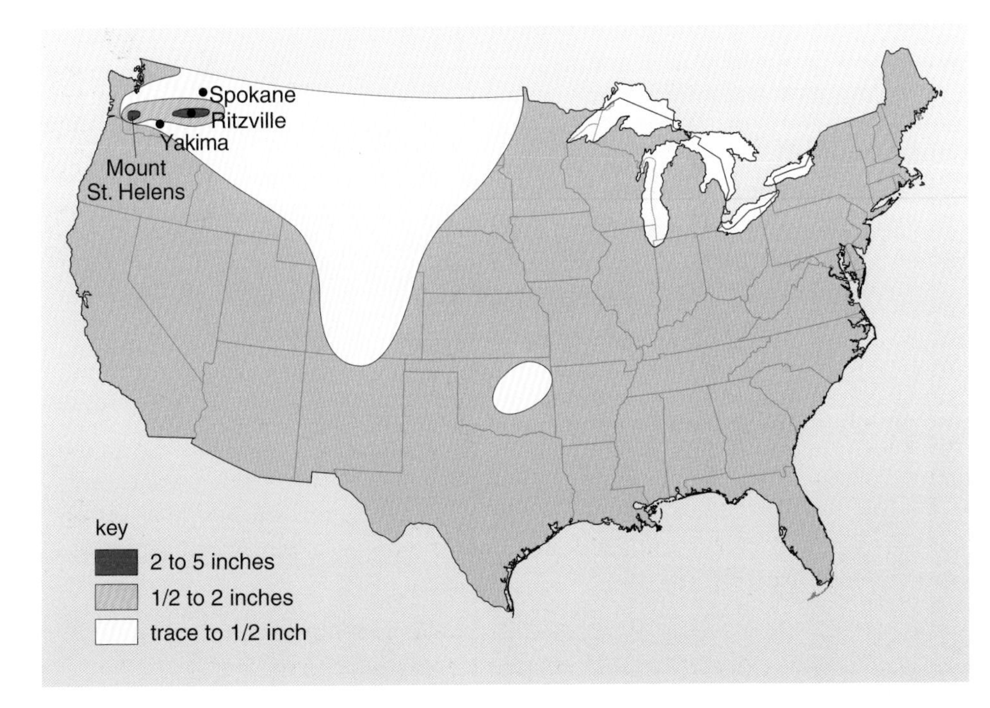

Figure 5.5 Thickness distribution of airfall from the 18 May 1980 eruption of Mount St Helens (1 inch ≈ 2.5 cm).

The collapse of a volcano (or, more usually, part of it) links volcanology with tsunami studies. A debris avalanche is a hazard in its own right but, if it enters the sea or a lake, it can cause a tsunami that is capable of taking lives even on a distant shore. So-called 'megatsunamis' caused by the collapse of a large part of a volcanic island (Figure 5.6) are a matter of controversy. Collapses definitely occur because giant debris avalanche deposits have been mapped on the ocean floor (for example TYVET Figure 4.13), but scientists don't know whether such events are generally rapid enough to cause a serious tsunami.

- ■ By what methods can volcanic activity cause tsunamis other than a debris avalanche or giant landslide?

- □ By underwater explosions, by pyroclastic flows entering the water, and by the collapse of a submarine caldera.

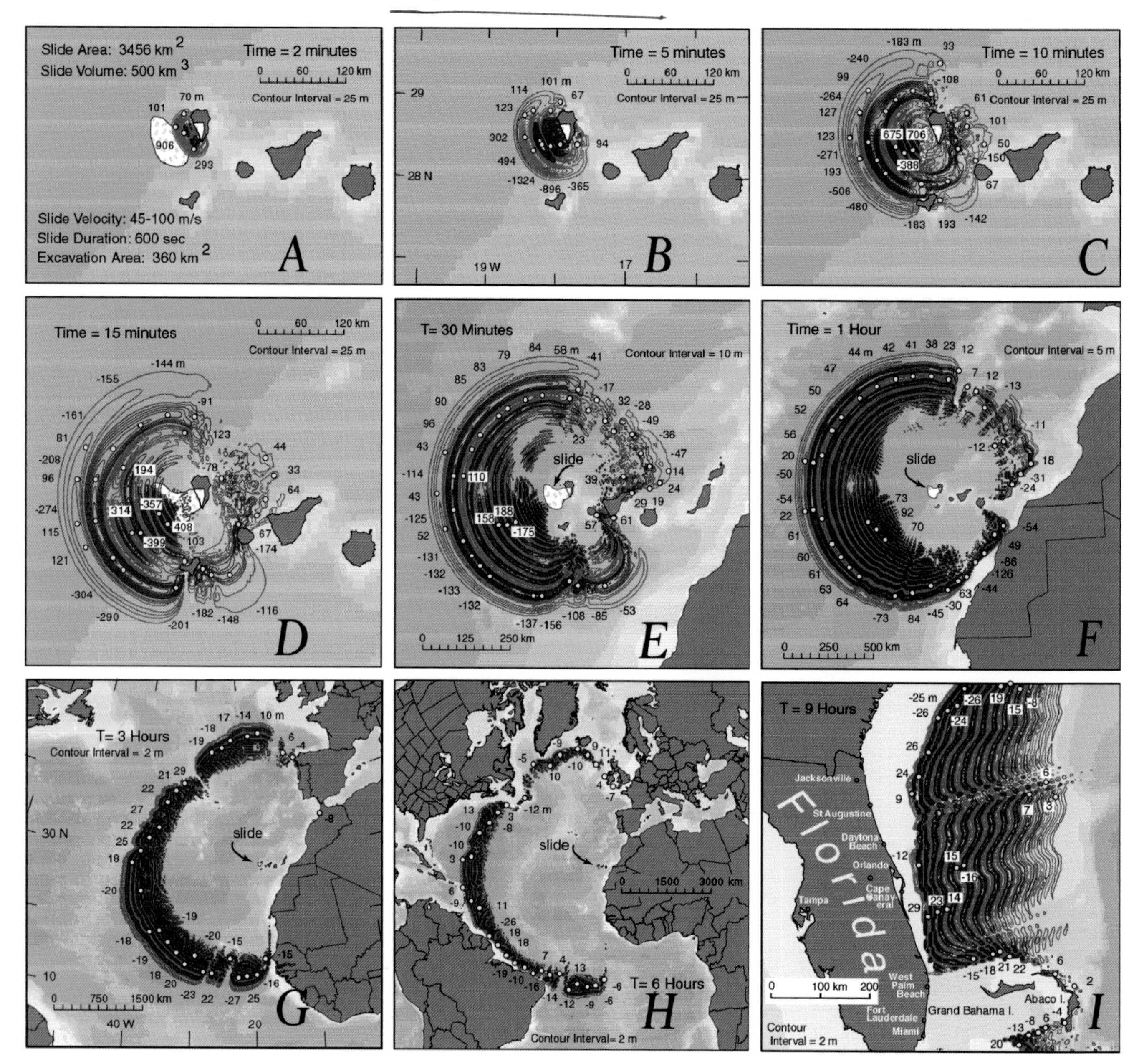

Figure 5.6 Output of a computer model showing the possible effect of a collapse of Cumbre Viejo in La Palma generating a megatsunami in the Atlantic Ocean. Numbers are height in metres at the point corresponding to the nearest yellow dot; red is above normal (wave crests) and blue is below normal (wave troughs). (TYVET Figure 5.17 is frame H in this sequence.)

Box 5.1 Contoured information on maps

On maps, and on many kinds of two-dimensional plots where the value of a quantity changes from place to place, it is common to show lines (contour lines) that link places of equal value. You may be familiar with topographic maps on which contour lines link points of equal height above sea level. In Figure 5.5, contour lines have been drawn linking all points of equal thickness of the airfall deposited by a particular eruption. The outer contour marks the limits of where ash was found. The next contour in encloses the area where more than half an inch of ash was deposited, and the innermost contour encloses the area where more than 2 inches of ash were deposited. The thickness of the deposit between one contour line and the next must be a value somewhere between the values on the lines. In this example, the thickness range is indicated by colour coding (according to the key on the map) rather than by labelling the contour lines.

You will see other examples of contoured information later in the course.

You will learn more about tsunamis in Chapter 11 but please see Box 5.2 for a note on the word *tsunami*.

Box 5.2 One tsunami, two tsunamis?

Tsunami is in origin a Japanese word. The Japanese language has no plural form for most nouns, so some English authors use *tsunami* interchangeably for both singular and plural. That does not look right to me. In this course I treat tsunami as a naturalised English word, and write *tsunamis* so it is always clear when I am referring to more than one. I think you would be very surprised if instead of *lahars* I used the Indonesian plural of *lahar*, which is *laharlahar*.

The eruption that claimed most lives in the 100 years before this course was written was the 1985 eruption of Nevado del Ruiz in Colombia, which caused a lahar that annihilated the town of Armero. Chapter 8 looks at the incompetence or ignorance (make your own judgement) surrounding the authorities' failure to evacuate the town. You will also see an example of a current lahar hazard map for Mount Rainier.

A jökulhlaup (if you pronounce it 'yer-kul-h-loip' you won't be far wrong) is in some ways a dilute equivalent of a lahar. It consists of a violent flood of water transporting rocks, gravel and often blocks of ice, but the nature of the material available at its source means that it lacks the high load of ash and/or mud that distinguishes a lahar. You will study a jökulhlaup in Activity 5.2.

Gas emitted from volcanoes poses many problems. It can blight land downwind from a persistently active volcano (Figure 5.7), poison the grazing after a large eruption, and accumulate in depressions or flow downhill to asphyxiate people. When you visit the Global Volcanism Program website you will probably see gases identified by their chemical formula rather than name, so they are listed for you here in Table 5.1. With the exception of water vapour and hydrogen fluoride, these gases are all denser than air so, if emitted passively (rather than being expelled in a hot and therefore buoyant eruption column), they will tend to flow downhill. You will learn more about the impact of volcanic gases in Chapter 6.

(a) (b)

Figure 5.7 Contrasting conditions (a) away from and (b) beneath the persistent sulfur dioxide plume from the Masaya volcano in Nicaragua (colour versions of TYVET Figure 5.23).

Table 5.1 Chemical formula of common volcanic gases.

Name	Formula
carbon dioxide	CO_2
hydrogen fluoride	HF
water vapour	H_2O
hydrogen sulfide	H_2S
sulfur dioxide	SO_2

Now do Activities 5.1–5.3 and then answer Questions 5.1–5.5, to consolidate and test your understanding of this chapter. Please don't look at the discussions of these activities or the answers to the questions until you have tried them yourself.

Activity 5.1 The Nyiragongo eruption in 2002

(The estimated time for this activity is 30 minutes.)

The notes for this activity are in the Study Guide.

Activity 5.2 The Grimsvötn jökulhlaups

(The estimated time for this activity is 15 minutes.)

The notes for this activity are in the Study Guide.

Activity 5.3 Long Valley skier fatalities in 2006

(The estimated time for this activity is 10 minutes.)

The notes for this activity are in the Study Guide.

5.2 Chapter 5 questions

Question 5.1

Give at least three reasons why TYVET Table 5.2 (p. 107) would be an unreliable guide to the relative proportions of fatalities from various volcanic causes during the next 100 years.

Question 5.2

If you were at the foot of an erupting volcano, and wanted to escape with your life, would you rather see a lava flow or a pyroclastic flow heading towards you, and why?

Question 5.3

List the different ways in which a pyroclastic flow can be initiated, and for each case cite one example of a specific eruption where this occurred.

Question 5.4

Describe the hazards associated with ongoing airfall, and any relevant preventive measures. (*One sentence per hazard*)

Question 5.5

Describe one way in which a lahar can begin *during* an eruption, and one way in which a lahar can begin *after* an eruption. Give a recent example in each case. (*One sentence for each*)

Chapter 6
Volcanoes and climate

Now read Chapter 6, where you will learn how volcanic eruptions can affect the climate, and even threaten civilisation. You should find more hazards to add to the table which you began in Chapter 5. Return here when you reach the end of the chapter.

6.1 Discussion of Chapter 6

6.1.1 The stratosphere

This chapter refers to the 'stratosphere' without defining it. It should be clear from the context, if not from your general knowledge, that the stratosphere is a layer above the lower atmosphere. Figure 6.1 shows that the atmospheric layers are defined by temperature; in the lower atmosphere (the 'troposphere') temperature decreases with height. This is where 'weather' occurs, because the temperature gradient allows convection to occur. Although the troposphere is the

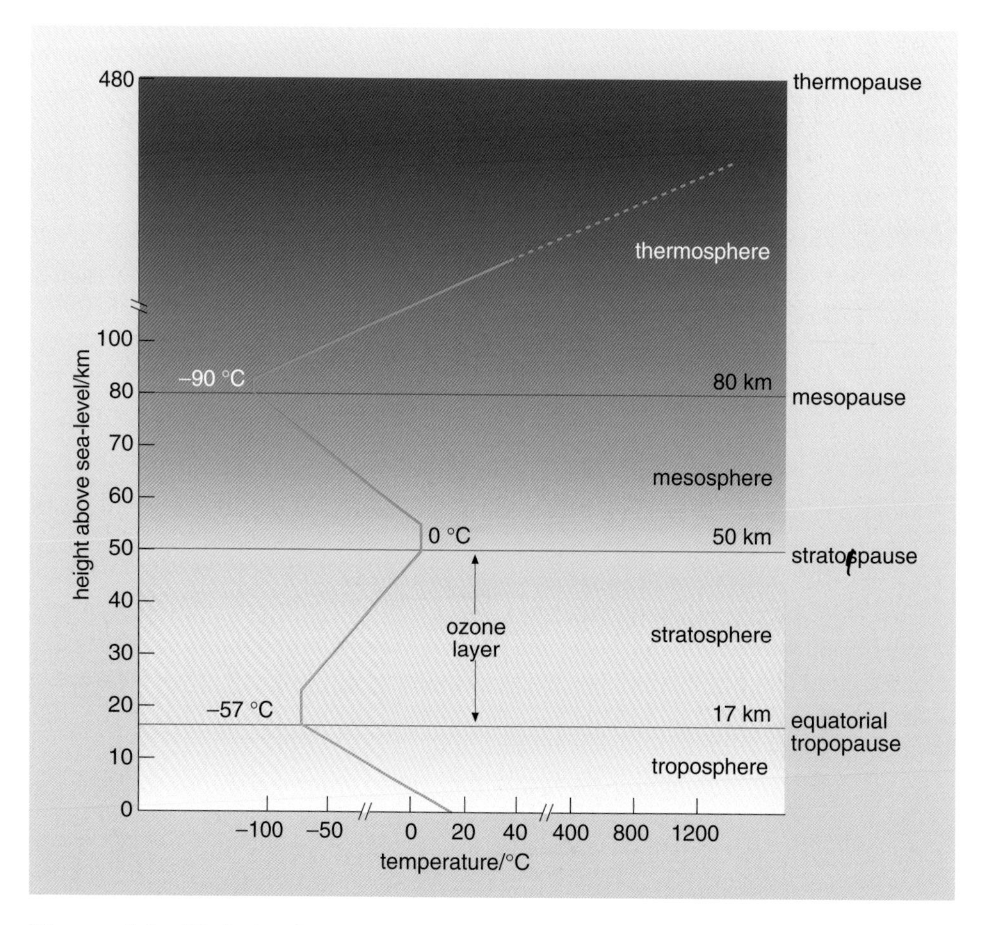

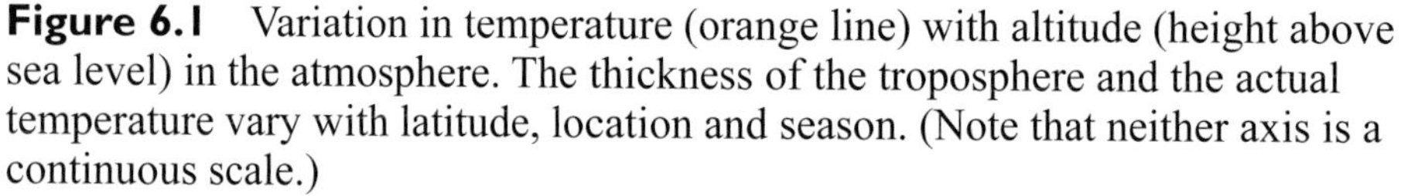

Figure 6.1 Variation in temperature (orange line) with altitude (height above sea level) in the atmosphere. The thickness of the troposphere and the actual temperature vary with latitude, location and season. (Note that neither axis is a continuous scale.)

thinnest layer of the atmosphere, it contains about 80% of the total mass, because pressure, and hence density, decrease with height throughout the atmosphere. Above the top of the troposphere, the temperature *increases* with height in a layer (thicker than the troposphere) called the stratosphere. Patterns of circulation in the stratosphere are important in controlling climate, and tend to be more stable than those within the troposphere. Two more reversals of temperature gradient define the outer (highly rarefied) layers, which do not concern us here.

The reason why temperature decreases with height in the troposphere is that the air there is warmed by proximity to solar-heated ground. On the other hand, warming of the stratosphere occurs by direct absorption of solar radiation, notably of ultraviolet radiation in the upper part of the stratosphere. See Box 6.1 for some background on the relationship between ultraviolet and other sorts of radiation which you will meet in Chapter 7.

Box 6.1 The electromagnetic spectrum

The light to which human eyes are sensitive is electromagnetic radiation, but only a small part of the full spectrum is visible (Figure 6.2). Electromagnetic radiation consists of electric and magnetic vibrations travelling at the speed of light. This radiation is usually described in terms of the distance between successive peaks in the vibration, which is known as the wavelength (waves are described in Box 7.1).

Visible light ranges in wavelength from 400 nm (violet) to 700 nm (red). Wavelengths that are too short for you to see are called ultraviolet (even shorter wavelength radiation is called X-rays). Ultraviolet radiation can damage your skin, so it is fortunate that most of the solar ultraviolet radiation is absorbed before it reaches the ground. Wavelengths that are too long for you to see are called infrared, then microwaves, and then radio waves.

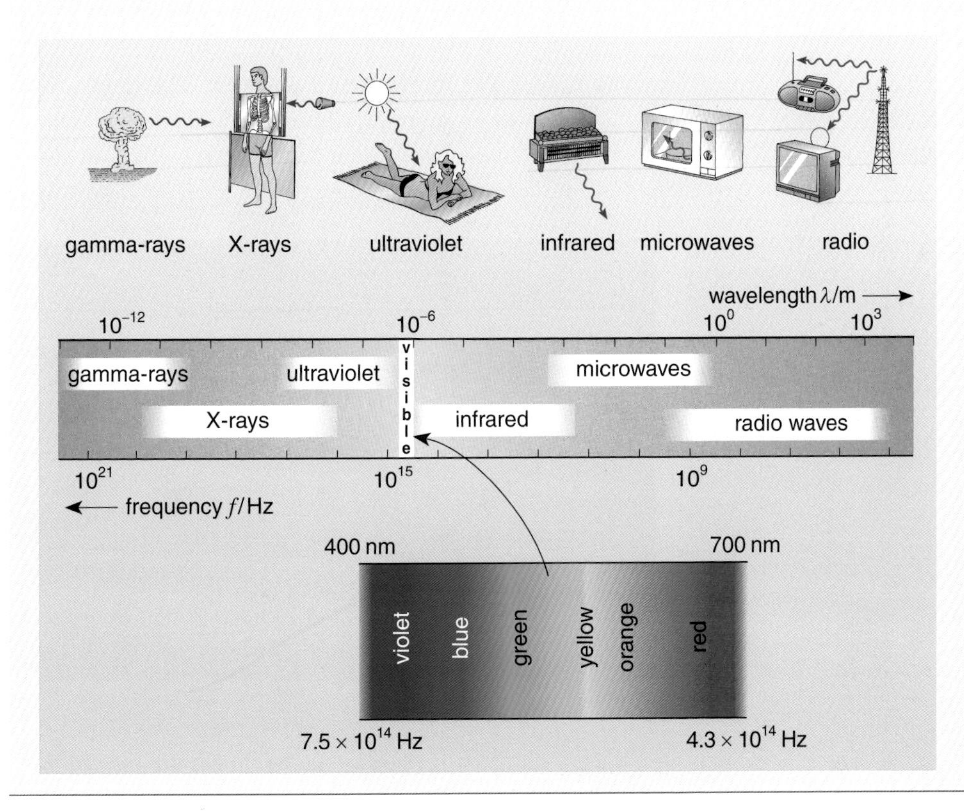

Figure 6.2 The electromagnetic spectrum, showing how visible light is only a tiny proportion of the whole: nm stands for nanometres; 1 nm = 10^{-9} m, which is one-millionth (10^{-6} m) of a millimetre. Hz (hertz) is the unit of frequency of the vibration, and tells you how many vibrations happen per second.

6.1.2 Historic eruptions

You probably didn't expect to read quotations from Benjamin Franklin in this course. He had a formidable intellect. As well as his observations of the Laki 'dry fog', which came relatively late in his long life, he invented flippers for swimmers, a heat-efficient stove, bifocal spectacle lenses and (after experiments in which he flew a kite during a thunderstorm to confirm the electrical nature of lightning) the lightning conductor to protect buildings from lightning strikes. Figure 6.3 gives some idea of the extent of the basalt lava field erupted by the 1783 Laki fissure eruption, which you also read about in Chapter 5.

Figure 6.3 View of the (now partly grass-covered) lava field erupted by the 1783 Laki fissure eruption, Iceland. All of the low ground is covered by lava, and the fissure from which it erupted is marked by a line of cinder cones stretching away towards the distant ice cap.

The 1815 eruption of Tambora is the most recent VEI 7 eruption. The next most recent eruption of comparable size was of the poorly known Baitoushan volcano straddling the China–Korea border, which produced a 5 km-wide caldera in about AD 1030. Figure 6.4 shows both of these from space.

(a)

(b)

Figure 6.4 (a) Tambora in Indonesia: a clearer view than in TYVET Figure 6.1. (b) Baitoushan in China: the caldera is the irregular snow-filled depression. Both photographs were taken by astronauts on the International Space Station. Each caldera is about 5 km across.

It is a matter of controversy whether the red sunsets painted by J. M. W. Turner (Figure 6.5a) genuinely illustrate the distant atmospheric effects of the 1815 Tambora eruption, because of recent claims that Turner had both partial colour-blindness and cataracts. However, a series of colour sketches by William Ashcroft (Figure 6.5b) is held to be a faithful record of the aftermath of the 1883 Krakatau eruption. Incidentally, the explanation of why sunsets (and sunrises) are red is that the lower the Sun in the sky, the greater the amount of atmosphere that the light has to pass through, and so the more the light is scattered by particles (importantly in this case, volcanic ash and aerosols) within the atmosphere. Red light is scattered least, and so the sunlight reaching the eyes of a ground-based observer becomes progressively redder as a greater proportion of the shorter wavelengths of light is scattered away.

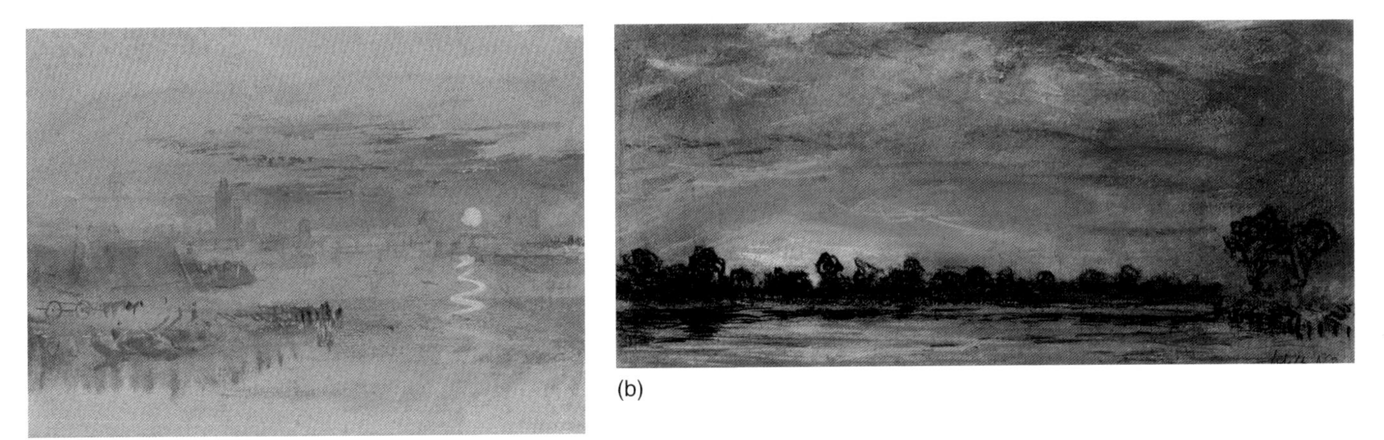

(a)

(b)

Figure 6.5 (a) A sunset by J. M. W. Turner, believed to have been painted circa 1830–40, but possibly inspired by the spectacular sunsets after the 1815 Tambora eruption. (b) 'Sunset at Chelsea, 14 July 1886' by William Ashcroft; part of a series that was a deliberate attempt to record atmospheric phenomena after the 1883 Krakatau eruption.

It is not straightforward to determine a 'global average temperature' in a way that enables one year to be compared with another. During the 19th century, measurements by thermometers gradually become more widespread but were far from evenly spaced, so it is problematic to know how to average out these measurements in a meaningful way. However, the fraction of a degree of global cooling claimed for the eruptions of Tambora (1815) and Krakatau (1883) is credible. The advent of measurements from space in the late 20th century improved the situation but, even so, the temperature drops attributed to El Chichón (1982) and Mount Pinatubo (1991) are blips on a noisy curve (Figure 6.6) because there are many factors other than volcanic eruptions affecting the temperature (notably oscillations in the circulation pattern of the equatorial Pacific Ocean, known as the El Niño effect).

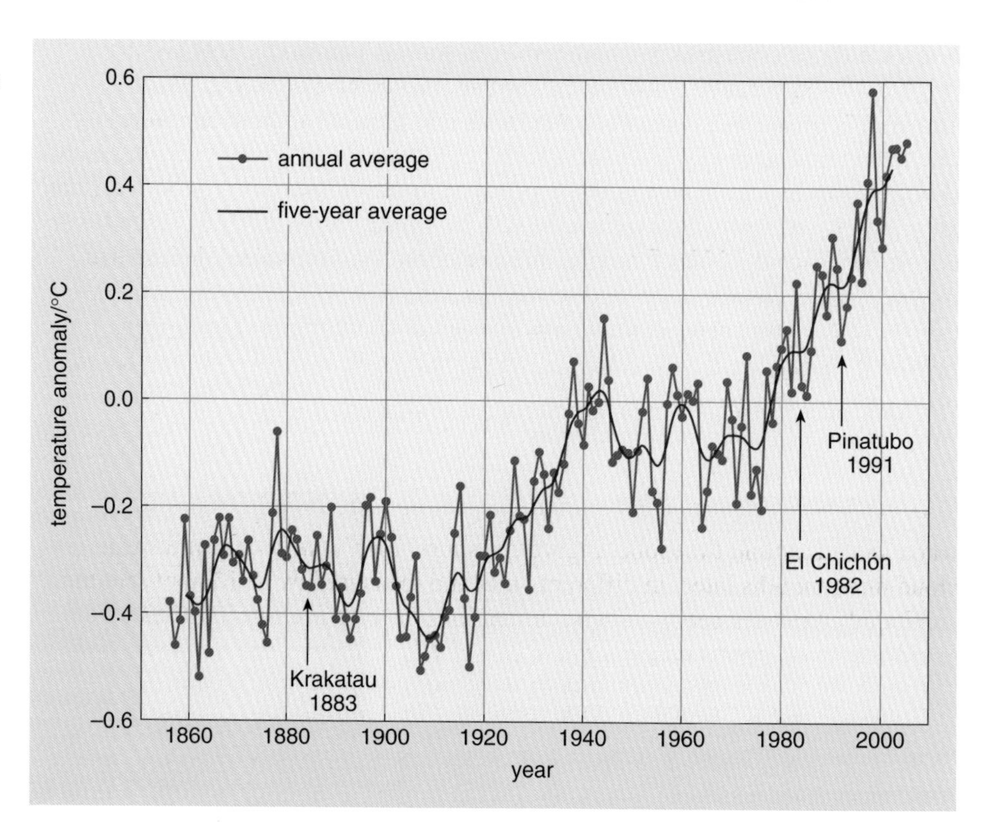

Figure 6.6 Global average temperature since 1856. The rise since about 1980 is generally attributed to 'global warming' caused by human activities. Annual minima can be recognised corresponding to the three major eruptions indicated, but there are many other dips requiring other explanations. (You can find help with reading graphs in Section 12 of the Maths Skills ebook.)

Images and other data collected by satellites are very useful for tracking the atmospheric dispersal of eruption products (Figure 6.7). You will read a little more about this in Chapter 7.

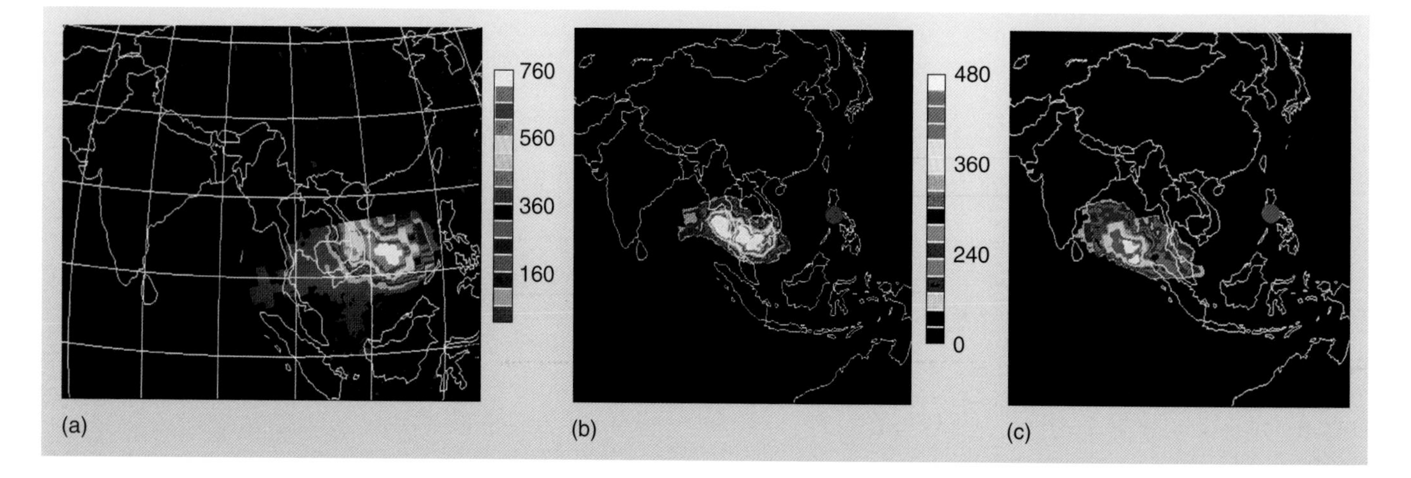

Figure 6.7 The sulfur dioxide cloud from Mount Pinatubo (marked by the red dot) measured on (a) 16, (b) 17 and (c) 18 June 1991 by a satellite instrument called the Total Ozone Mapping Spectrometer (colour versions of TYVET Figure 6.2). The colour scale is in conventional units called 'mill atm cm', which correspond to how thick (in thousandths of a centimetre) the layer of sulfur dioxide gas would be if collected together in pure form at sea level. The key for (b) and (c) is the same.

The strange units 'milli atm cm' in Figure 6.7 were invented by Professor G. M. B. Dobson (1889–1976) of Oxford University (originally for recording the amount of atmospheric ozone), and are sometimes more conveniently referred to as 'Dobson Units'.

■ In the densest part of the Pinatubo sulfur dioxide cloud on 17 June 1991, how thick a layer could be formed by collecting all the sulfur dioxide into a pure layer at sea level?

□ According to the colour scale in Figure 6.7b, the densest part of the cloud is between 450 and 480 'milli atm cm'. So this (hypothetical) layer would be between 450 and 480 thousandths of a centimetre thick, i.e. 0.45–0.48 cm or 4.5–4.8 mm thick.

This doesn't sound much but it is enough to have a measurable effect even when spread around the globe. Figure 6.8 shows the Pinatubo sulfur dioxide cloud three months later (in different units and measured by a different satellite technique). You will see time-lapse animations of the Pinatubo sulfur dioxide cloud when you do Activity 6.1 at the end of this chapter.

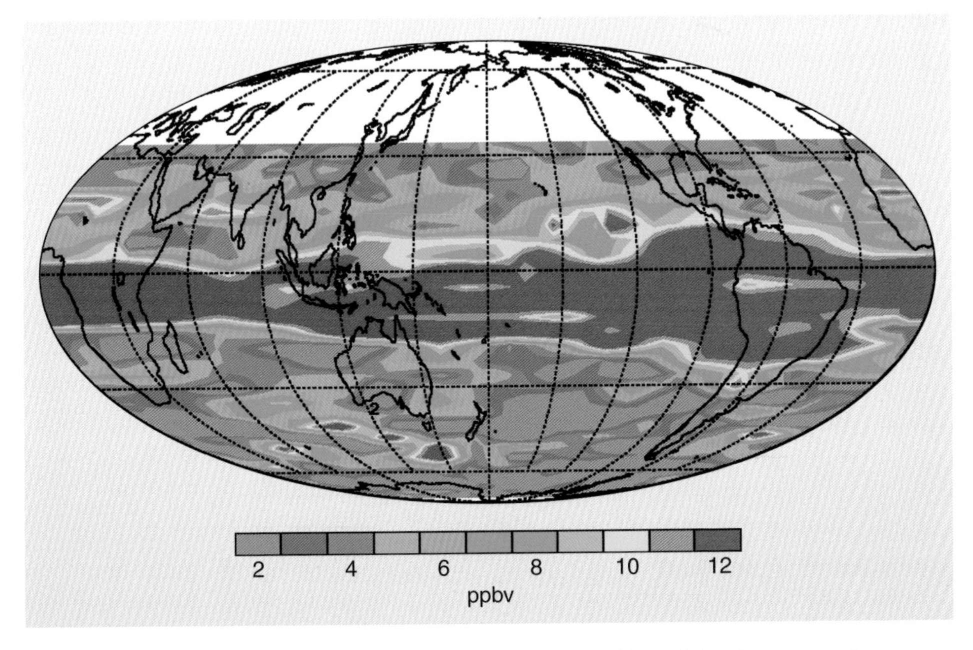

Figure 6.8 The sulfur dioxide concentration at 26 km altitude, mapped on 21 September 1991 by the Microwave Limb Sounder instrument onboard NASA's Upper Atmosphere Research Satellite. (The unit ppbv is parts per billion by volume.)

After the discussion of El Chichón and Mount Pinatubo, Chapter 6 begins to describe more ancient eruptions, beginning with those that upset the climate recently enough to have been experienced by humans, and working back to rarer and more devastating eruptions that are, fortunately, so infrequent that humans have not yet had to survive one. Ice cores provide a valuable record of changing levels of atmospheric sulfur dioxide that can be correlated with volcanic eruptions. Figure 6.9 is an example that includes many of the eruptions you have met, plus prominent spikes in the years 639, 1100 and 1257, which are not discussed in TYVET and for which other evidence and suggested eruption sites are particularly uncertain. The term 'acidity spike' is used because when sulfur dioxide dissolves in water, it essentially makes (weak) sulfuric acid.

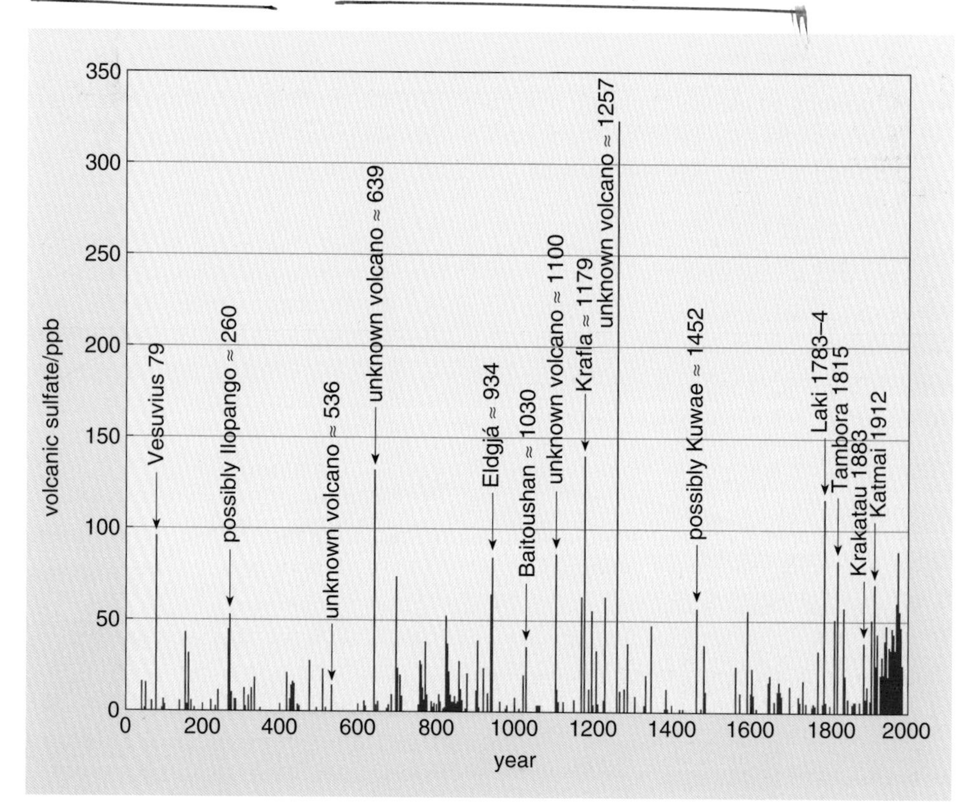

Figure 6.9 The 2000-year record of volcanic sulfate (acidity) in a Greenland ice core (ppb = parts per billion, which is a measure of concentration).

6.1.3 Prehistoric eruptions and supervolcanoes

There is no standard, worldwide division between 'history' and 'prehistory' because written records begin at vastly different dates in different parts of the world. For example, although the eruption of Santorini in about 1620 BC coincides with mythical times even in the classical Mediterranean world, there are records preserved in China that may reflect hemispheric climate disturbance caused by that eruption. However, the beauty of the VEI scale is that it is based on the volume of material erupted and, provided the deposits and/or any resulting caldera can be identified and mapped out, the volume of a prehistoric eruption can be estimated almost as accurately as that of a modern one.

The Toba eruption of 74 000 years ago is the largest identified eruption since humans emerged as a species, and TYVET refers to genetic evidence (which is beyond the scope of this course) indicating that, at about the same time, humans were virtually wiped out. This should serve as a salutary warning about the possible consequences when a supervolcano erupts (as one inevitably will) at some unpredictable time in the future. As should be apparent from TYVET Figure 6.4, there is a wide range of uncertainty about how much sunlight would be blocked by a Toba-style eruption and how long the darkness would last. However, even if it was not dark enough to deny plants the sunlight necessary for growth, a global temperature drop of about 10 °C in the first year would be highly likely, remaining several degrees below normal for at least five years. Therefore, quite apart from near-total devastation across much of the continent where the eruption took place, there would be crop failure and famine affecting the entire globe. The death toll would be vast, and it is not unthinkable that civilisation would collapse under the strain.

Incidentally, the term 'supervolcano' has an interesting history, which is noted in Box 6.3.

Box 6.3 Who invented 'supervolcanoes'?

Although 'supervolcano' is a simple and natural-sounding term, it is a recent invention. Casual use of the expression 'super-volcanic' can be traced back to work in the 1970s on Yellowstone. The term 'super-eruption' was first coined in the title of the paper 'Volcanic winter and accelerated glaciation following the Toba super-eruption' which appeared in the famous science journal *Nature* in 1992, written by Mike Rampino and Steve Self, two of the contributors to the 'Volcanoes and the atmosphere' video you will watch in Activity 6.1. However, the earliest public use of 'supervolcano' appears to have been in a television programme in the BBC2 science series *Horizon* entitled 'Supervolcanoes', first broadcast in the UK in February 2000.

Today, some volcanologists are happy to use the word 'supervolcano', whereas others dislike it, even if they agree that 'super-eruption' is a catchy and appropriate term to describe a VEI 8 event.

If you are studying this course in the British Isles, you may be surprised to learn that you live within easy reach of a continental flood basalt province. This is the North Atlantic (or Brito-Arctic) province (see TYVET Table 4.1) which was erupted about 57 million years ago. Splendid exposures can be seen in the Giant's Causeway on the coast of Antrim in Northern Ireland and in the Inner Hebrides in Scotland, such as the example in Figure 6.10. The greater part of the on-land area of this province lies in Greenland, which was adjacent to Scotland at the time. The eruption of this enormous basalt field was a precursor to the rifting that caused the North Atlantic Ocean to open.

The North Atlantic continental flood basalts do not, like several other examples, coincide with a mass extinction event. Activity 6.2 gives you an opportunity to look into this matter a little deeper, but first do Activity 6.1 and answer

Figure 6.10 Cliffs fringing the island of Staffa in Scotland, revealing the interior of a single, 60 m thick flow unit within the 57 million-year-old North Atlantic flood basalt province. The base of the flow coincides with the cave roof. The lower part of the flow developed beautiful vertical columnar joints during cooling. In the upper part of the flow, the jointing developed differently (colour version of TYVET Figure 4.23).

Questions 6.1–6.6 to consolidate and test your understanding of this chapter as a whole.

Activity 6.1 'Volcanoes and the atmosphere' video

(The estimated time for this activity, including Questions 6.1 and 6.2, is 45 minutes.)

The notes for this activity are in the Study Guide.

6.2 Chapter 6 questions

Question 6.1

According to the 'Volcanoes and the atmosphere' video, the climate effect of a particular eruption depends on which two factors?

Question 6.2

What was Haraldur Sigurdsson's explanation in the 'Volcanoes and the atmosphere' video for how the fluorine gas emitted by the 1783 eruption of Laki killed so much (75%) of Iceland's livestock?

Question 6.3

During the 1783 Laki eruption the volume of basalt erupted was about 15 km^3. How much smaller is this volume than that of the smallest flood basalt province in TYVET Table 4.1?

Question 6.4

Bearing in mind their respective latitudes, and any other relevant information, attempt to explain why the 1991 sulfur dioxide cloud from Mount Pinatubo affected *both* hemispheres whereas the 1982 cloud from El Chichón spread only in the Northern Hemisphere. (If you don't have an atlas for checking latitudes, you can find this information conveniently on the 'summary' page for each volcano on the Global Volcanism Program website.)

Question 6.5

In TYVET section 'Volcanoes and human history', the AD 180 eruption of Taupo in New Zealand is said to have been a VEI 6 eruption with an erupted volume of 30 cubic kilometres. Attempt to work out whether '30 cubic kilometres' falls within the erupted volume range for VEI 6 eruptions specified in TYVET Table 3.1.

Question 6.6

'The death toll would be vast, and it is not unthinkable that civilisation would collapse under the strain', according to Section 6.[illegible].3. Imagine that you are supreme ruler of a major country or (if you have sufficient ambition!) even of the entire world. What would *you* do, if anything, to prepare for a supervolcanic eruption that will probably happen sometime in the next 100 000 years? Consider this for a while, and write down a few notes before looking at the answer.

Now please do one more quick activity to conclude your study of this chapter.

Activity 6.2 Flood basalts, mantle plumes, and mass extinctions

(The estimated time for this activity is 15 minutes.)

The notes for this activity are in the Study Guide.

Chapter 7
Monitoring volcanoes

Now read Chapter 7, where you will learn about the main techniques used to study volcanic activity. Question 7.2 involves completing a table, and you may find it particularly convenient to work on this while studying the relevant part of the chapter. Return here when you reach the end of the chapter.

7.1 Discussion of Chapter 7

7.1.1 Volcano observatories

The staffing levels of volcano observatories and the quantity and quality of instruments available to them vary considerably around the globe. For example, the reports of the 2006 Home Reef eruption, which you saw in Activity 4.1, were contributed mostly by people on passing yachts rather than by professional volcanologists; much of the information on the 1996 Grimsvötn eruption in Activity 5.2 came from the Nordic Volcanological Institute, which is effectively Iceland's volcano observatory; and some of the information in the report in Activity 5.3 was courtesy of the Long Valley Observatory. You will see more information from volcano observatories in Chapter 8.

7.1.2 Seismic techniques

Seismic monitoring was introduced as the single most valuable tool for studying volcanic events. Of course, it is vital in logging and interpreting tectonic earthquakes too. Beyond saying that seismometers 'detect vibrations', TYVET does not explain how they work. It is fairly easy to understand the principle behind a seismometer (Figure 7.1). A mass is suspended freely from a frame that is secured to the ground so that, when the ground shakes, carrying the frame with it, the mass remains stationary with the frame vibrating about it. A full record requires that, in addition to up-and-down motion (Figure 7.1a), the seismometer also records horizontal vibration (Figure 7.1b). Horizontal movement can be in any direction, but can be fully documented by two horizontal vibration detectors arranged at right angles: for example, one to record north–south vibration and the other to record east–west vibration.

These days, rather than using the relative motion between mass and frame to make a chart recording, seismic data are recorded digitally, using electronics to measure the changing force necessary to move the mass in time with the frame (rather than letting the frame vibrate about it). This is how the seismometer in

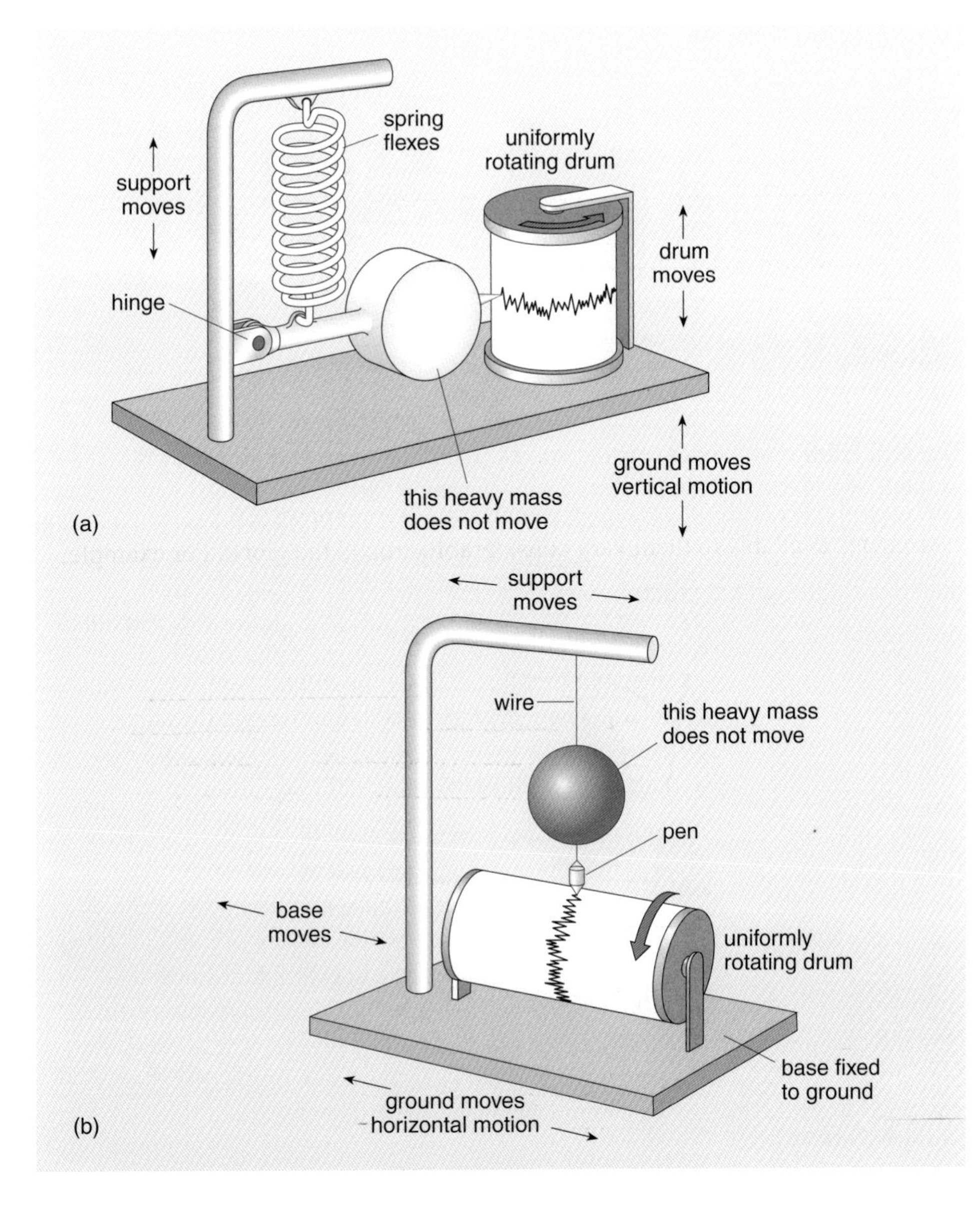

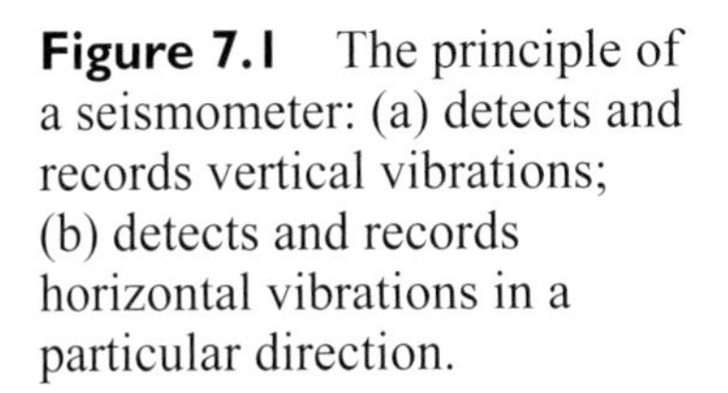
Figure 7.1 The principle of a seismometer: (a) detects and records vertical vibrations; (b) detects and records horizontal vibrations in a particular direction.

Figure 7.2 works. Collecting data in this way makes for easy transmission from a remote seismometer to an observatory, but the principle is the same as shown in Figure 7.1. Simple seismometers record only up–down vibration, and where you see a single seismometer trace (as in TYVET Figures 7.3 and 7.4) it is probably a record of up–down vibration. However, three-component seismometers (up–down, north–south and east–west) are becoming more common.

Figure 7.2 (a) Installation of a seismometer (in the foreground hole which the cable disappears into) on the lower flanks of Villarica, a Chilean composite cone volcano. (b) The seismometer in the hole, before burial. The soil here is volcanic ash.

You will learn more about seismic waves (the phenomenon that causes the ground, or a seismometer, to vibrate) in Chapter 9. For now, Box 7.1 gives you some basic information about waves, which is relevant to describing seismograph traces such as TYVET Figures 7.3 and 7.4 and to describing seismic waves as they travel through the ground.

Box 7.1 An introduction to waves

Anything that repeatedly goes up and down can be described in terms of waves. The obvious example is the surface of the sea, but the same principle applies to pressure (for example, sound waves in air), various sorts of vibration in the ground (seismic waves and the trace recorded on a seismograph), and the intensity of electric and magnetic fields (in electromagnetic radiation, such as light).

There are two common ways to represent a wave in a diagram. One is to show how the value of the variable property changes with distance (Figure 7.3). In the case of water waves, this would be like an instantaneous cross-section through the sea surface. In the case of seismic P-waves, this would be a graph of pressure variations (compression and dilation) measured along the direction of wave travel. The *wavelength* is defined as the distance between successive wave crests. The *amplitude* is half the height between a peak and a trough.

The other way is to show how the variable property measured at a single, stationary point varies over time (Figure 7.4). In the case of water waves, this is like a graph of how a floating object would bob up and down. In the case of a seismometer trace, this would typically be a graph of displacement (vertical or sideways) over time. The *period* is defined as the time it takes for successive wave crests to arrive. The amplitude is the same as before.

It is often more convenient to think in terms of how many waves arrive per second, rather than quote the wave's period, particularly when dealing

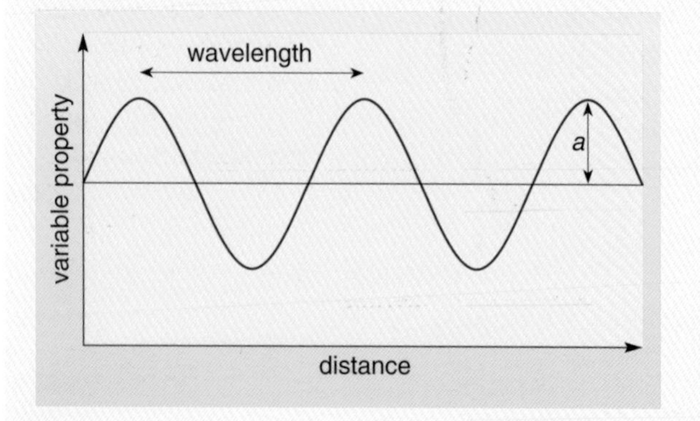

Figure 7.3 A wave varying with distance (a = amplitude).

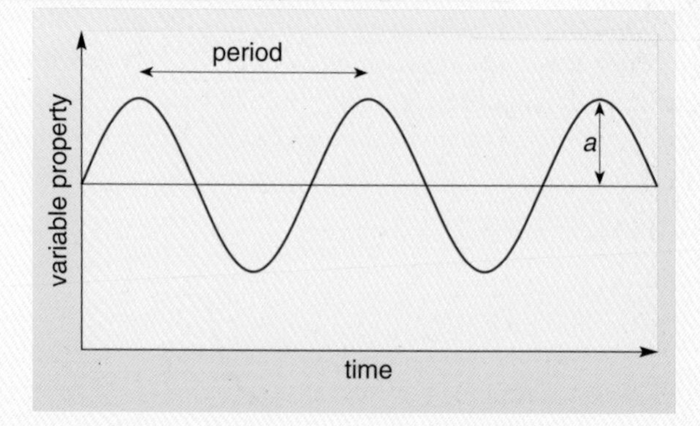

Figure 7.4 A wave varying with time (a = amplitude).

with waves whose period is only a fraction of a second. This is called *frequency*, which is measured as vibrations per second and sometimes referred to by the internationally recognised scientific unit called hertz (abbreviation Hz). The relationship between period and frequency is very simple: frequency per second = 1/(period in seconds).

■ If the period of a wave is 0.05 seconds, what is its frequency?

□ The answer is simply 1/(0.05 seconds) = 20 per second = 20 hertz.

Frequency does not have to be a whole number: for example, a wave with a period of exactly 0.06 seconds has a frequency of 16.667 hertz.

There are two further points to note.

1. The time between the arrival of successive wave crests gets less – so the frequency *increases* – as the wavelength decreases. For waves of a given speed, the relationship is frequency = speed/wavelength.
2. Waves are a way of transporting *energy* but there is no net movement of *matter*. For example, a wave crossing an ocean does not carry any water with it; the disturbance (and hence energy) is propagated across the ocean by means of the sea surface bobbing up and down. However, when the wave has passed, all the water is back where it started. Likewise, seismic waves in the Earth carry energy, for example from the source of an earthquake to a place where energy carried by the waves does some work, which can be as mild as making a seismometer needle vibrate or as violent as shaking a building into ruins.

Seismic tomography is briefly mentioned on TYVET p. 172. This is a powerful modern technique for mapping subsurface structure, but it needs many events to build up a picture so it cannot be used to monitor rapid changes. An impressive tomographic view of the magma chamber below the Yellowstone caldera is shown in Figure 7.5.

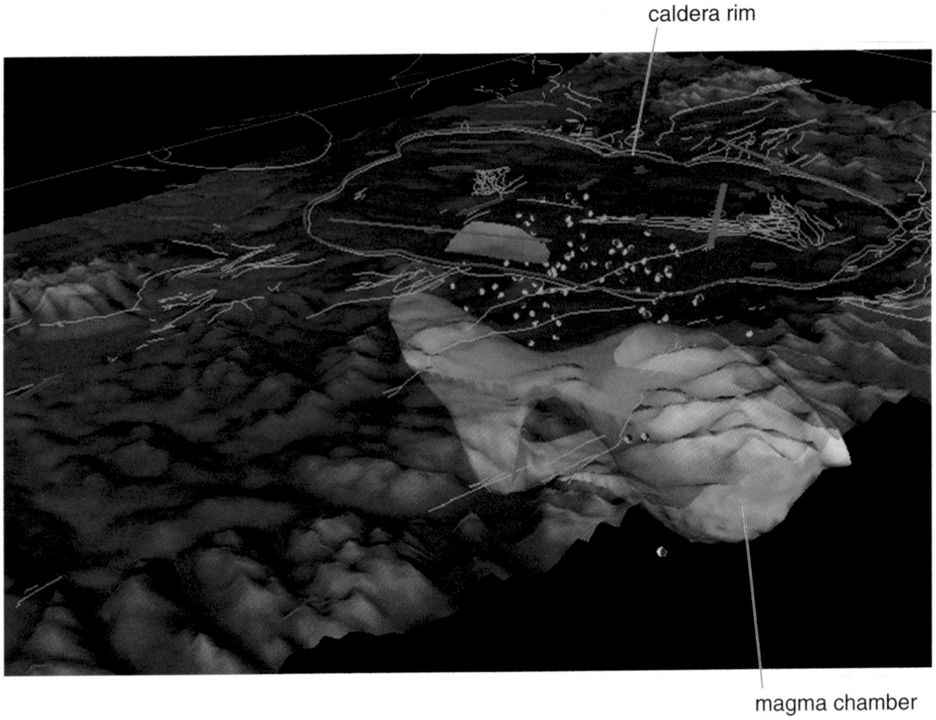

caldera rim

magma chamber

Figure 7.5 Three-dimensional oblique perspective view of Yellowstone National Park, USA. There is much information in this view. Surface topography has been made transparent to reveal the magma chamber (inferred from seismic tomography). The caldera outline is traced in red on the overlying ground surface, faults are green, and the directions of gradual surface movement (based on GPS surveying) are shown by pink arrows.

7.1.3 Ground deformation

TYVET mentions several types of instrument other than seismometers that can be installed on a volcano to record and transmit data to an observatory. Pictures of them can be rather repetitive because, basically, there is a 'black box' containing the instrument (which is often buried) connected via cables to an antenna and powered by solar panels and batteries. Figure 7.6 shows a tiltmeter in a spectacular location. It also shows why even the most reliable instruments need attention from field personnel to keep them working.

(a) (b)

Figure 7.6 A tiltmeter station on the lava dome of Mount St Helens: (a) in September 2005; (b) in January 2006, during snow removal to re-expose the solar panels to sunlight. The meter is buried and the tube merely houses the batteries and supports the antenna and solar panels. Mount Rainier is visible in the background.

In contrast, monitoring by satellites can be done without ever visiting the volcano, although experience shows that it is wise to seek ground-based insights as well. Obtaining data, especially images, using satellites or aircraft is called *remote sensing*. There is a whole section on this topic at the end of Chapter 7, but the first example of remote sensing is in the section 'Ground deformation' where TYVET Figure 7.9 shows a radar interferogram of Mount Etna. This reproduces poorly in black-and-white, so a colour version is shown here (Figure 7.7). In this course, you are not expected to understand how radar interferometry works, merely that, in the right situation, it can detect local height changes of little more than a centimetre between one radar image and the next (which can be weeks, months or years apart).

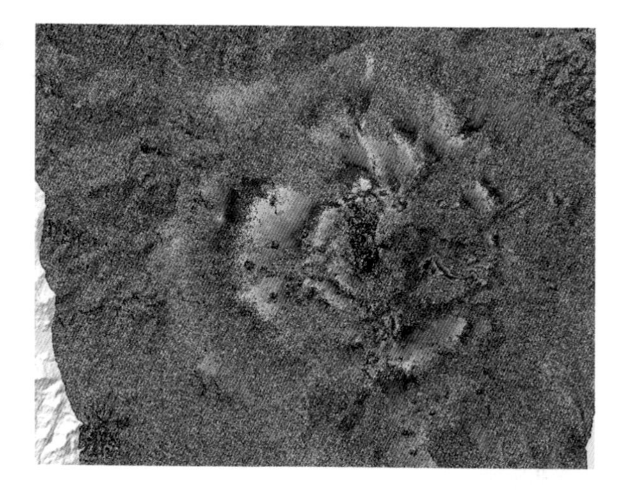

Figure 7.7 Radar interferogram of an area 30 km wide centred on Mount Etna, showing changes in surface elevation between November 1993 and January 1998. Each colour fringe corresponds to a height change (in this example, subsidence) of 28 mm (colour version of TYVET Figure 7.9).

Another approach to mapping height changes on a volcano is by means of GPS. You saw a team of volcanologists doing this simultaneously with microgravity measurements in TYVET Figure 7.11. It is important to measure height above sea level during gravity surveys, because gravity depends not just on the mass of rock (or magma) below you but also on your distance from the Earth's centre. Subsidence of 5 m would cause the local gravity to increase by one part in a million even if no magma had been added below your feet, and gravity meters are sufficiently sensitive to detect a change of less than one part in *ten* million, so you need to know your height to within a few centimetres in order to interpret a gravity change correctly. Gravity meters are both delicate and expensive, and it is not practical to deploy a permanent network of enough remotely-operating gravity meters to collect data with sufficient spatial density to construct a map of gravity changes. Hence the need for repeated field surveys using a mobile instrument to reoccupy a network of stations at intervals typically ranging from months to years.

7.1.4 Infrasound monitoring

Infrasound, or infrasonic, monitoring is mentioned briefly but not illustrated in TYVET, so an example is shown here in Figure 7.8. You can think of infrasound as either very low frequency sound waves or as rapid pressure changes, originating at a volcanic explosion.

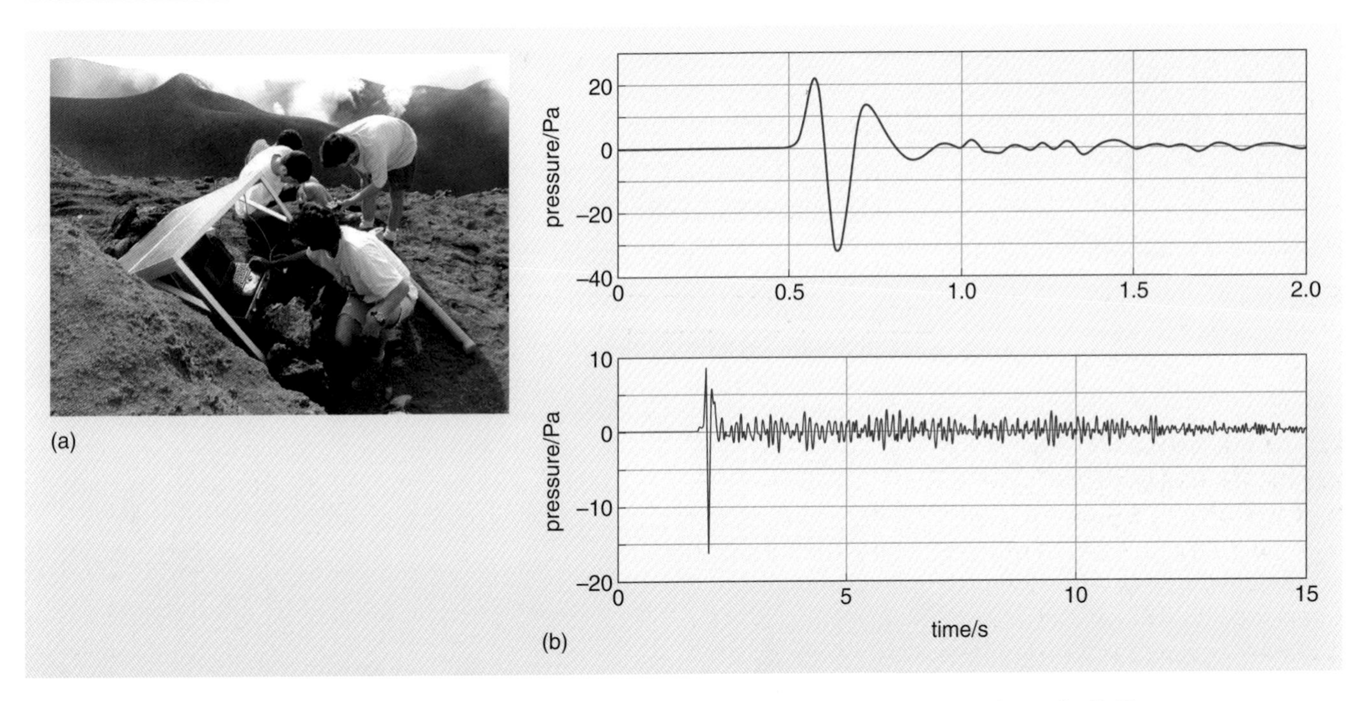

Figure 7.8 (a) The hub station for a temporary array of four infrasound detectors on Stromboli. Detectors, connected to this hub by cable, record infrasound pulses, and the time difference for detection at each station allows the position of the source to be located. (b) Typical infrasound signals from explosions at Stromboli's two active craters: top, from a crater mostly out of view beyond the right of (a); bottom, from the crater in the background of (a).

The units of pressure in Figure 7.8b are pascals (abbreviation Pa). It is pressure *change* that is recorded, not total atmospheric pressure.

■ Atmospheric pressure is close to 10^5 Pa. What is the maximum pressure change recorded in Figure 7.8b as a fraction of this?

□ The maximum change is in the upper trace, going from +20 Pa to −30 Pa, so the total change is 50 Pa. As a fraction of the total atmospheric pressure, this is $50/10^5 = 50 \times 10^{-5} = 5 \times 10^{-4}$. This is five ten-thousandths of the total atmospheric pressure.

Infrasonic pressure changes are thus fairly slight and can rarely be felt by bystanders. The pressure change is greater the closer you are to the source, which is more than 200 m away in Figure 7.8.

Figure 7.9 A tripod-mounted Differential Optical Absorption Spectrometer measuring the gas plume from Stromboli. The cloth shades the laptop screen from the bright sunlight so the operator can read the display.

7.1.5 Gas monitoring

There is quite a lot about gas monitoring in Chapter 7. The easiest volcanic gas to detect from a distance is sulfur dioxide because its concentration can be judged by the strength of absorption of very specific wavelengths of ultraviolet light. You should recall from Chapter 5 that sulfur dioxide poses a continual environmental hazard at persistently degassing volcanoes, as well as sometimes heralding an eruption. Fortunately, the new generation of instruments (Figure 7.9) are much more portable than the previous generation which occupied the entire passenger seat of a truck (TYVET Figure 7.13).

7.1.6 Thermal monitoring

Before starting this course, you could be excused for thinking that measuring the temperature of a volcano would be the most useful monitoring technique. This is not the case because the temperature at the surface (which is all you can measure) lags behind events in the interior because of the slow rate of heat conduction through rock, and it is influenced by multiple processes. In contrast, a seismic signal is a much clearer indicator of current activity. However, when hot rock or gas is suddenly exposed (for example, by an explosion), the temperature does correspond to a current event. Figure 7.10 is a good example of

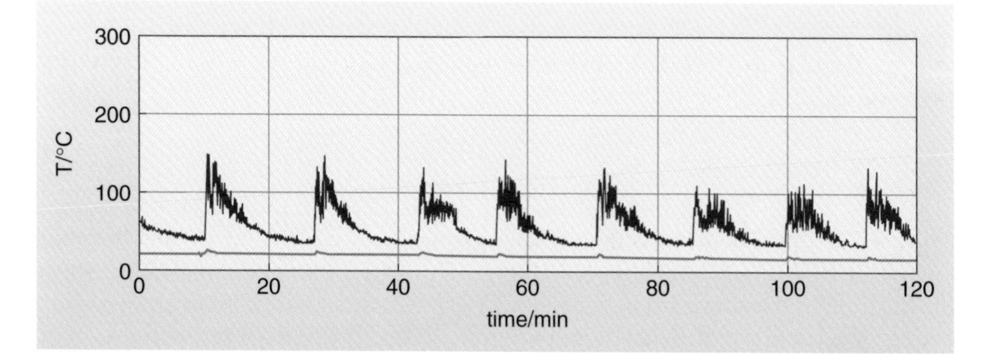

Figure 7.10 Temperatures sensed by 1° field-of-view (upper, red trace) and 60° field-of-view (lower, blue trace) infrared thermometers on the rim of Pu'u O'o crater on Kilauea, Hawaii in 2003. Pulses of hot gas barely register on the wide field-of-view thermometer. In contrast, they are clearly seen by the narrow field-of-view instrument, which was targeted directly at a vent on the crater floor, but even this does not register the true temperature because some of the colder background remains visible through the partly transparent hot gas and because the vent is smaller than the field of view.

this; it shows a two-hour extract of the temperature log from two of the infrared thermometers in TYVET Figure 7.16. These detect infrared radiation in the broad 8–14 μm wavelength region of the spectrum. The output is usually reported as the temperature that would be necessary to provide the same amount of radiant energy if the whole field of view was uniform. This is not necessarily the case, because there are often small, very hot areas and large, cooler areas in the same field of view. In the figure, each sharp rise in temperature indicates a sudden release of gas (consistent with coalescence and collapse of a foam layer as in TYVET Figure 3.17), which tails off until the next event.

The abbreviation μm means micrometres: 1 μm = 10^{-6} m.

Infrared cameras capable of recording an image are expensive and are rarely left unattended in the field. Figures 7.11 and 7.12 give you a taste of what can be seen with such instruments when they are available.

Figure 7.11 Stromboli seen from a helicopter in May 2003: (a) ordinary visual view; (b) the same view with an image from a thermal camera superimposed. The thermal view sees through the steam cloud and reveals the size and location of fumarole vents on the inner crater wall.

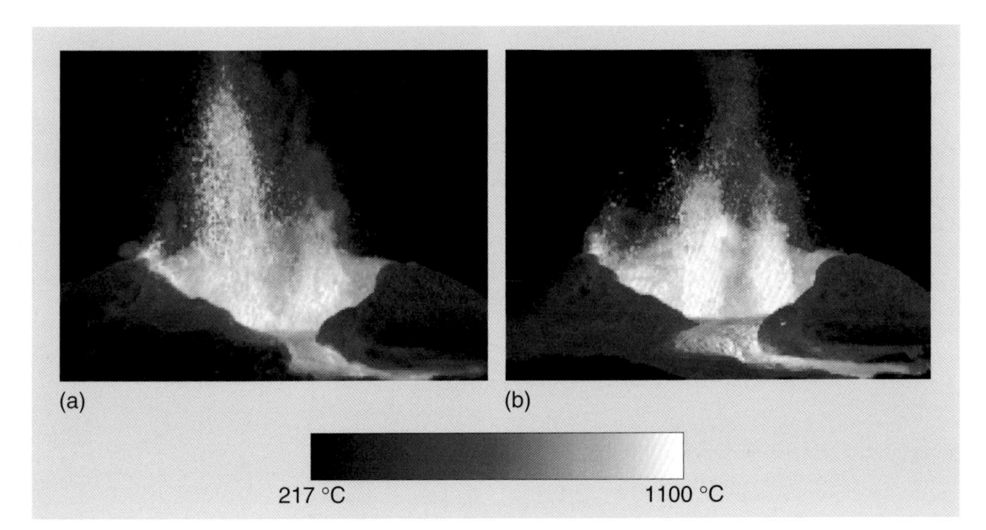

Figure 7.12 Single frames from an infrared (8–14 μm) video camera showing fire fountains at Piton de la Fournaise on Réunion Island in the Indian Ocean in August 2003. The height, structure and intensity of the fountains (from two discrete sources in this case) can be analysed, leading to an estimate of how far the lava flow issuing from the crater is liable to travel.

7.1.7 More remote sensing

Chapter 7 concludes with a discussion of remote sensing from satellites. In Figures 6.7 and 6.8, you saw examples of aerosol detection. This is because of the way in which sulfur dioxide absorbs certain very characteristic wavelengths of ultraviolet radiation. You have also seen plenty of images from space recorded in the visible part of the spectrum. Here examples of remote sensing at infrared wavelengths are considered, where temperatures both hot (best measured at shorter infrared wavelengths) and cold (at longer infrared wavelengths) dominate the picture. Figure 7.13 includes an image made by subtracting a thermal infrared image recorded at 11.3 μm from a simultaneous thermal image recorded at 10.3 μm. This is called the 'split window' technique and, because ash absorbs radiation more strongly at 10.3 μm than at 11.3 μm, it is an excellent way to detect diffuse clouds of volcanic ash, which cannot be distinguished from ordinary meteorological clouds in a single-wavelength image. The instrument used for this is called AVHRR, which stands for Advanced Very High Resolution Radiometer. This name is no longer appropriate because the instrument is neither advanced nor high resolution by modern standards, but it remains a valuable device and has been carried on a long series of weather satellites.

Drifting ash clouds, such as that in Figure 7.13d, are a major hazard to aircraft but they can be tracked on such images for several days, providing valuable information for VAACs. See Box 7.2 for a note on the conventions for reporting time in scientific or technical communications.

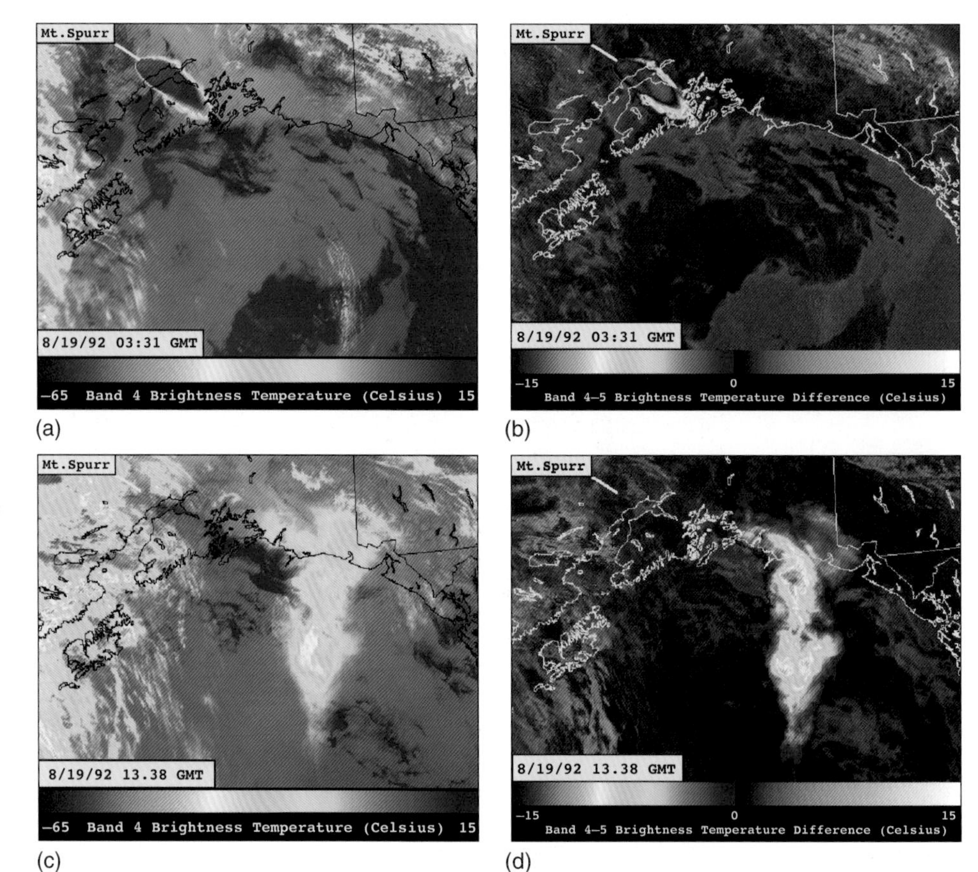

Figure 7.13 Weather satellite images of the eruption of Mount Spurr, Alaska, on 19 August 1992, recorded using an AVHRR instrument: (a) and (c) are 10.3 μm images ('band 4') and (b) and (d) are 'split window' images made by subtracting an 11.3 μm image from the 10.3 μm image ('band 4 – band 5'); (a) and (b) were recorded about 90 minutes after the start of the eruption. The eruption cloud-top is the highest, and hence coldest, feature in (a), and only its fringe is transparent enough to allow its ash content to manifest itself in (b); (c) and (d) were recorded 10 hours later, when the eruption has stopped and the cloud is drifting away. In (c) the eruption cloud looks no different from ordinary meteorological cloud but in (d) it is highly distinctive because of the peculiar signature of ash.

Box 7.2 What time is it?

Local time zones vary around the globe. When reporting events to the international community, sometimes the local time is used. However, for events whose effects are widespread, it is more usual to report the time according to an international standard called Universal Time (abbreviation UT). Sometimes this is called UTC (Coordinated Universal Time), but it is the effectively the same. This is also the same as Greenwich Mean Time (GMT), which is the civil time in the UK during the winter months. Volcanic Ash Advisory Centres use the same time system (expressed only as hours and minutes) indicated by the letter Z (which is 'Zulu' in the radio phonetic alphabet, hence the expression 'Zulu time'). So, if you see a time in hours, minutes and seconds, or just hours and minutes, accompanied by UT, UTC, GMT or Z, they all mean the same.

In the case of some remote volcanoes, even the very fact that there has been an eruption is known only from satellite images, which can also be used to document the duration of a poorly known eruption or to spot episodes of enhanced activity. Figure 7.14 shows examples from the MODIS thermal alert system, which you met near the end of Chapter 7.

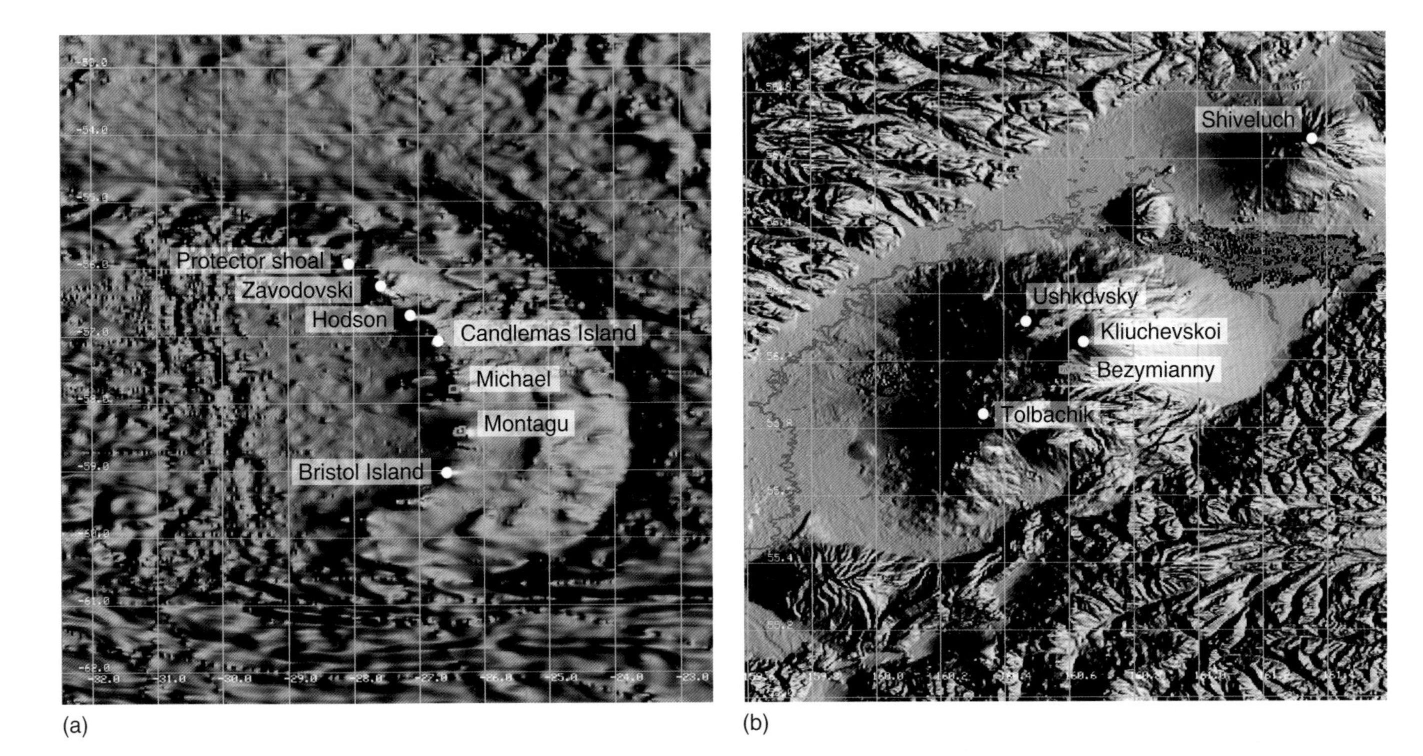

Figure 7.14 MODIS thermal alerts superimposed on a map base. (a) Twelve months of alerts for December 2005 until December 2006 for the South Sandwich Islands (map covering 10° of latitude or 1000 km), demonstrating otherwise virtually undocumented lava effusion at the volcano Mount Belinda on Montague Island, and presumed lava lake activity at Mount Michael on Saunders Island. (b) Alerts for 9 May 2006 on Bezymianny volcano in Kamchatka (map covering 2° of latitude or 200 km), recording a lava dome collapse.

7.1.8 Webcam monitoring

Remote cameras are mentioned in TYVET only in the section on lahar warnings (p. 179) and in the caption for Figure 7.16. However, more and more cameras are being deployed all the time, some in remote or dangerous locations and others at exceptionally good viewpoints. In many cases, volcano observatories (and other bodies) make the images available over the internet, although to save bandwidth it is rare to update the image more often than once every minute. Figure 7.15 shows data from a Mount St Helens 'webcam' situated on Johnston Ridge, near the site where Dave Johnston lost his life in May 1980 in the directed blast (Chapter 5). Before this course was written, several Open University students became interested in keeping track of activity on Mount St Helens through this webcam, and shared their observations on the online discussion forums. If this captures your interest too, Activity 7.2 will get you started.

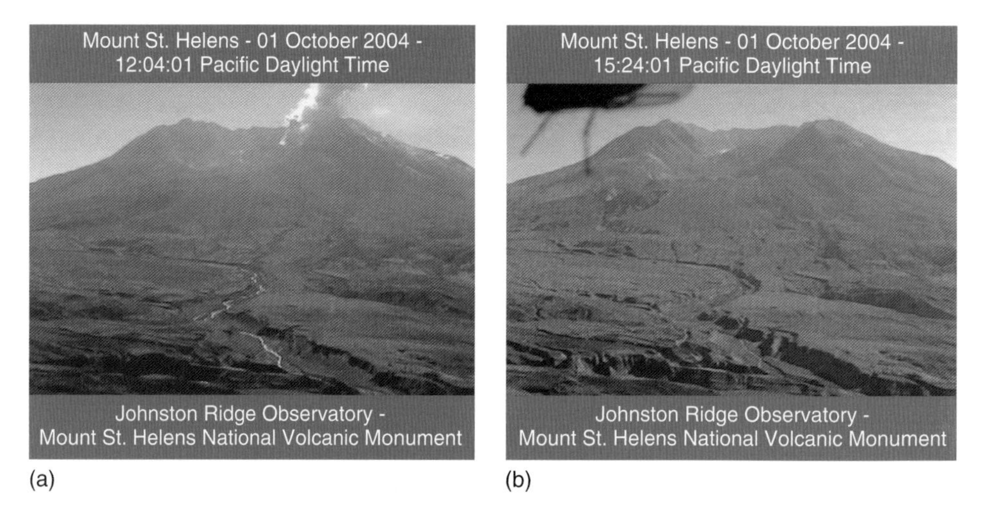

Figure 7.15 Webcam images of Mount St Helens on 1 October 2004: (a) a small steam and ash eruption from the side of the reactivating lava dome; (b) 3 hours later, the eruption over, a small visitor inspects the camera lens.

7.2 Chapter 7 questions

Now do Activities 7.1 and 7.2 and answer Questions 7.1–7.4, to conclude your study associated with this chapter.

Question 7.1

In what way, important for giving early warning of a major eruption, do volcanic eruptions differ from major tectonic earthquakes?

Question 7.2

Several types of volcanogenic earthquake are described in Chapter 7. Complete Table 7.1 below to show the processes believed to cause four of the main types. You should need only a few words in each case.

Table 7.1 For use with Question 7.2.

Type	Cause
high-frequency event	
low-frequency event	
volcanic tremor	
very long period events	

Question 7.3

What is RSAM, and why is it so useful?

Question 7.4

Why doesn't an increase in gravity measured on a volcano always indicate the arrival of magma filling in underground voids?

Question 7.5

Refer back to the description of height changes in the centre of the Yellowstone caldera in Chapter 6 (p. 158). Describe, *in one sentence*, these changes using terminology introduced in the section 'Ground deformation' in Chapter 7 (pp. 172–5). Explain, *in one or two sentences*, what additional data would be useful to support the assertion that 'magma may be moving in and out of this chamber'.

There are two internet-based activities associated with this chapter. You may be asked to extract some specific recent information from one or more websites such as these in the End of Course Assessment.

Activity 7.1 Visit a Volcanic Ash Advisory Centre (VAAC)

(The estimated time for this activity is 15 minutes.)

The notes for this activity are in the Study Guide.

Activity 7.2 Visit a volcano webcam

(The estimated time for this activity is 30 minutes.)

The notes for this activity are in the Study Guide.

Chapter 8
Living with volcanoes

In Chapter 8 the term 'probability' is used in a relatively formal way. Even if you managed to answer the probability part of Question 3.6 without any help, it will probably (pun intended!) be useful to read Box 8.1 before starting the chapter.

Box 8.1 Probability

When tossing a coin there is an even chance that the head or the tail will land face-up, i.e. each is equally likely. The probability of throwing a head is described mathematically as '1 in 2' or ½. Probabilities have a value between zero and one, and can also be expressed as a percentage of less than 100. A probability of one (or 100%) is a certainty and something with a probability of zero definitely will not happen. It can be more convenient to describe a probability of 0.1% as '1 in 1000' rather than as 0.001. You will find examples of all three uses in this course.

Specifically, this course is concerned with how often a particular event is likely to happen. For example, how often there will be an eruption with a certain VEI anywhere in the world (as in Question 3.6) or how often ash deposited by an eruption will exceed a certain thickness at a particular point on a map (one of the hazard examples in Chapter 8). In such cases you are dealing with *annual probability*.

For example, as you saw in Question 3.6a, there is about one VEI 6 eruption every 100 years. (This figure has been established by examining the geological record of eruptions spanning tens of thousands of years because, clearly, it would be unreliable to base the estimate on, say, just the most recent century, which could have been atypical.)

An occurrence of 'about one VEI 6 eruption every 100 years' can be expressed as an annual probability of 'about one in a hundred', 'about 1 in 100', 'about 1/100' or 'about 1%'. Note that this does *not* mean that VEI 6 eruptions happen regularly at about 100-year intervals. Probabilities like this cannot predict *when* an event is likely to happen; they are just a way of expressing how often, on average, such an event can be expected. There is no reason why there could not be two (or more) VEI 6 eruptions in the same year. For example, if Vesuvius in Italy were to have a VEI 6 eruption in 2010, that would have no bearing whatsoever on the likelihood of Mount Fuji in Japan having a VEI 6 eruption in 2010 also.

Now read Chapter 8, the final chapter focused on volcanoes, but return here when you reach the section 'Warnings and crisis management' (p. 198). This part of the chapter looks at various aspects of the relationship between people and volcanoes and also gives formal definitions of *hazard* and *risk* (they are not the same), which are equally applicable to earthquakes and tsunamis as they are to volcanic eruptions.

8.1 Discussion of Chapter 8, pp. 192–8

8.1.1 Hazard, risk and vulnerability

In case you are not clear yet, 'hazard' has different meanings according to the context. For example, airfall can be described as 'a volcanic hazard' but the hazard *posed by* airfall at a given location is (as stated in Chapter 8) the annual probability of airfall arriving at that location. Tackling the next question may help clarify this.

Question 8.1

Airfall poses a hazard in many different ways. Write down a list of the many different problems that airfall can cause.

Vulnerability is also a somewhat elastic concept. For example, the vulnerability of any realistic roof to collapse if only a millimetre of airfall lands on it is zero. (No one builds a roof *that* feeble; it would collapse as soon as rain fell on it, volcano or no volcano!) However, there are few flat roofs that can withstand tens of centimetres of accumulated airfall. Any consideration of the risk of roof collapse because of airfall must therefore take into account the *thickness* of airfall expected as well as any actions taken to make a roof less vulnerable to airfall damage. The latter can include making it more resistant in advance (by building it stronger and/or with a steeper pitch) and actions taken during ashfall (such as sweeping the roof clear to prevent a dangerous accumulation). In the end, it does not matter whether the expected thickness of airfall is factored into the hazard (as in Figure 8.1) or regarded as an aspect of vulnerability, as long as it is included somewhere in the overall assessment of risk. Read Box 8.2 if the meanings of the contoured areas in Figure 8.1 are unclear.

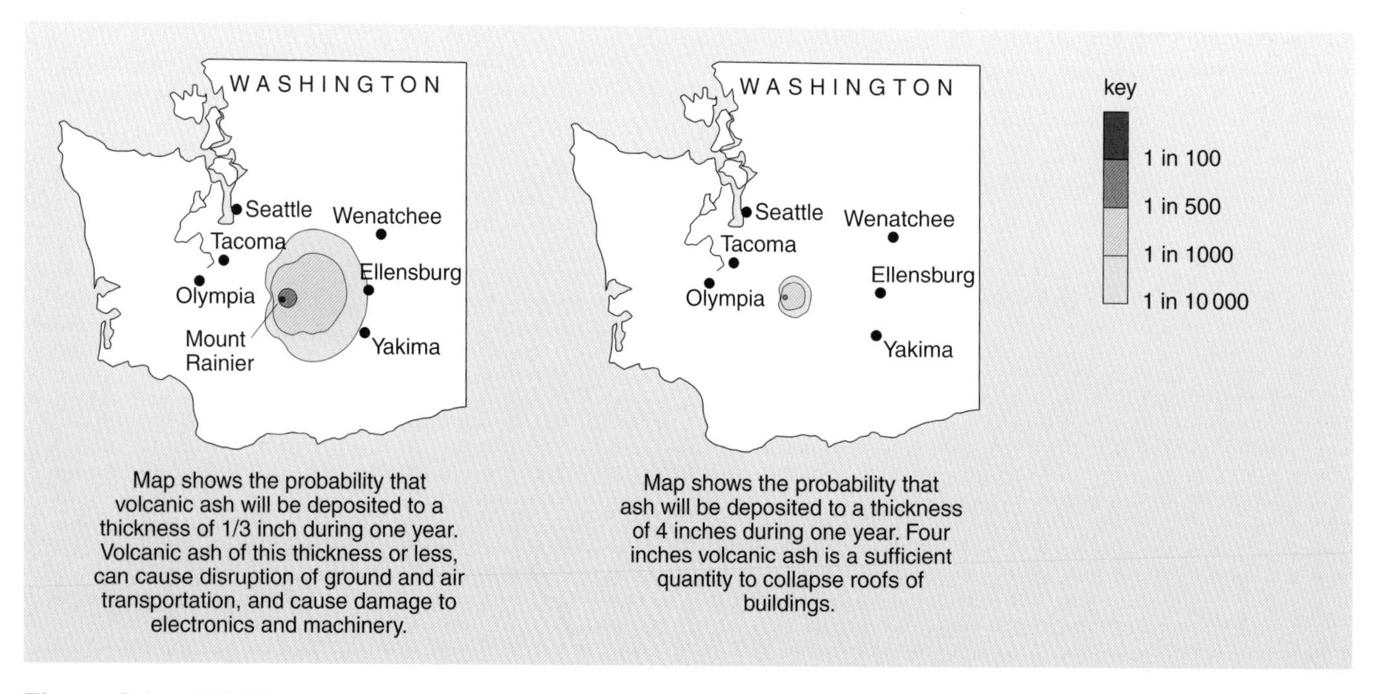

Figure 8.1 Airfall hazard maps for the region of Washington State around Mount Rainier, showing the geographic distribution of hazard (expressed as annual probability) of two different airfall thicknesses (colour version of TYVET Figure 8.3.): 1/3 inch is a little less than 1 cm; 4 inches is about 10 cm.

When there are several active volcanoes in a region, it can be more useful, especially from the perspective of people responsible for land-use regulation, evacuation planning, etc., to have a map that combines the hazard (of a particular type) from *all* volcanoes that could affect the area. Figure 8.2 shows an example.

■ Based on Figure 8.2, which one of the Cascades volcanoes is regarded as the most active (as far as eruptions leading to airfall are concerned)?

□ The probability of airfall is shown as strongest around Mount St Helens, which is because this has been assessed to be the most active volcano. (However, other volcanoes do affect the pattern: for example, Mount Rainier distorts the 0.1% contour on the 10 cm ashfall plot.)

Box 8.2 Annual probability contours on maps

In Figure 8.1, contour lines have been drawn linking all points where the annual probability of a certain thickness of airfall is identical. The area between each contour line has been coloured differently to make the pattern clearer. So, on the left-hand map in Figure 8.1, the outermost contour line is where the probability is 1 in 10 000. Outside that line the probability is less than 1 in 10 000. Between that line and the next one in, (which is the 1 in 1000 contour), in the zone coloured green, probability must increase from 1 in 10 000 at the outer edge to 1 in 1000 at the inner edge. The next zone in (coloured pink) has a probability between 1 in 1000 at its outer edge and 1 in 500 at its inner edge.

Similar principles apply in Figure 8.2, except that the annual probabilities are expressed as percentages.

■ What is a 0.01% annual probability, expressed as 'one in something'?

□ 0.01% as a fraction is 0.01/100, which is the same as 0.1/1000 = 1/10 000, so it can be expressed as 'one in ten thousand'.

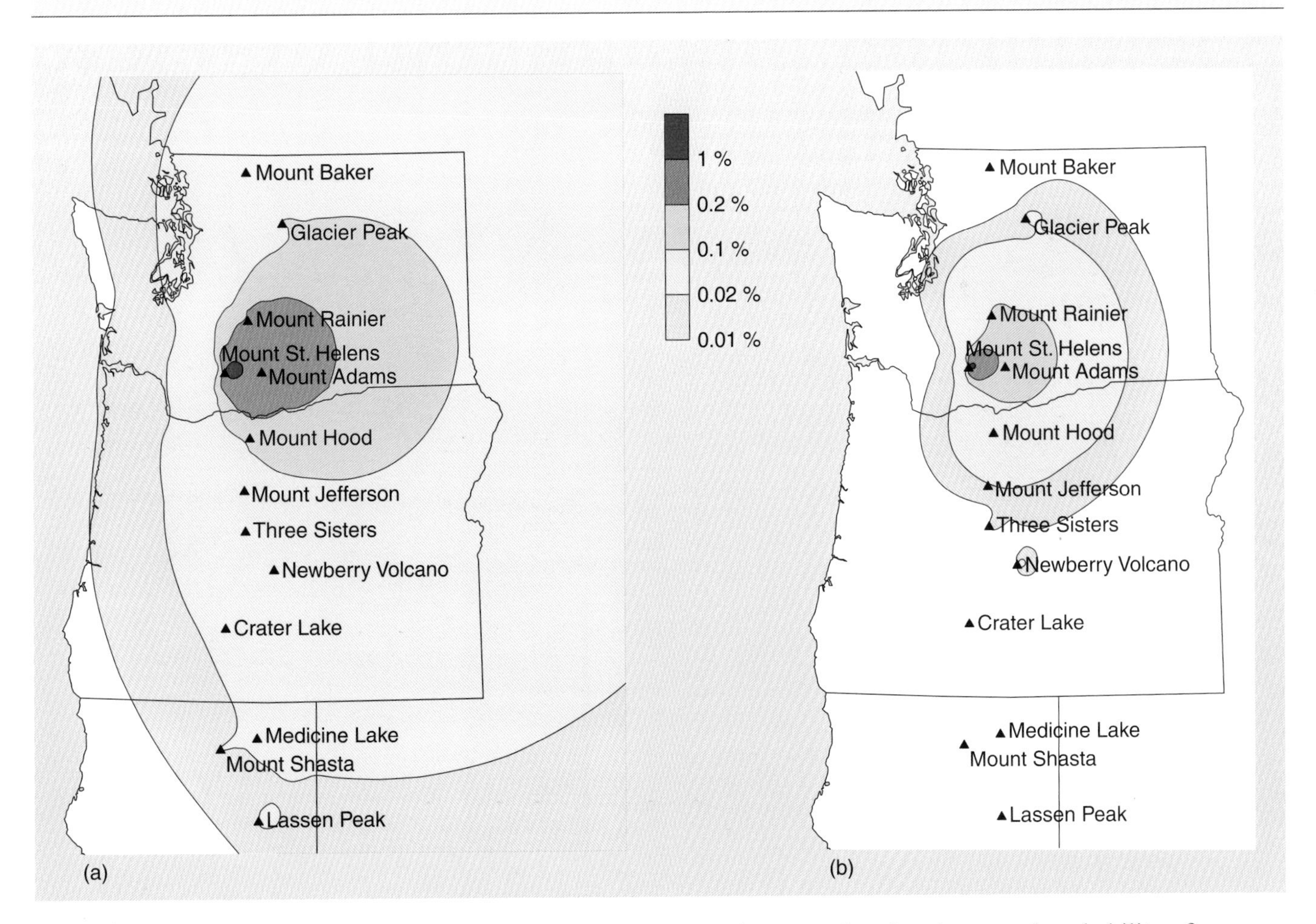

Figure 8.2 Combined airfall hazard maps for the whole Cascade range, showing the annual probability of (a) 1 cm ashfall and (b) 10 cm ashfall. (Note that 0.1% here means the same as 1 in 1000 in Figure 8.1.)

■ Look carefully at the airfall probability patterns in Figures 8.1 and 8.2. How would you describe the patterns and can you suggest an explanation?

□ The patterns are not symmetrical about the volcanoes; instead, they are displaced to the east. The explanation is that, most of the time, the wind blows from the west, as was the case during the 18 May 1980 Mount St Helens eruption (Figure 5.5).

The probability of wind from different directions, and of different wind speeds, therefore has to be taken into account in preparing hazard maps such as Figures 8.1 and 8.2.

Figure 8.3 shows a slightly different approach to hazard mapping. Instead of plotting the annual probability of a given thickness, it shows (for lahars, rather

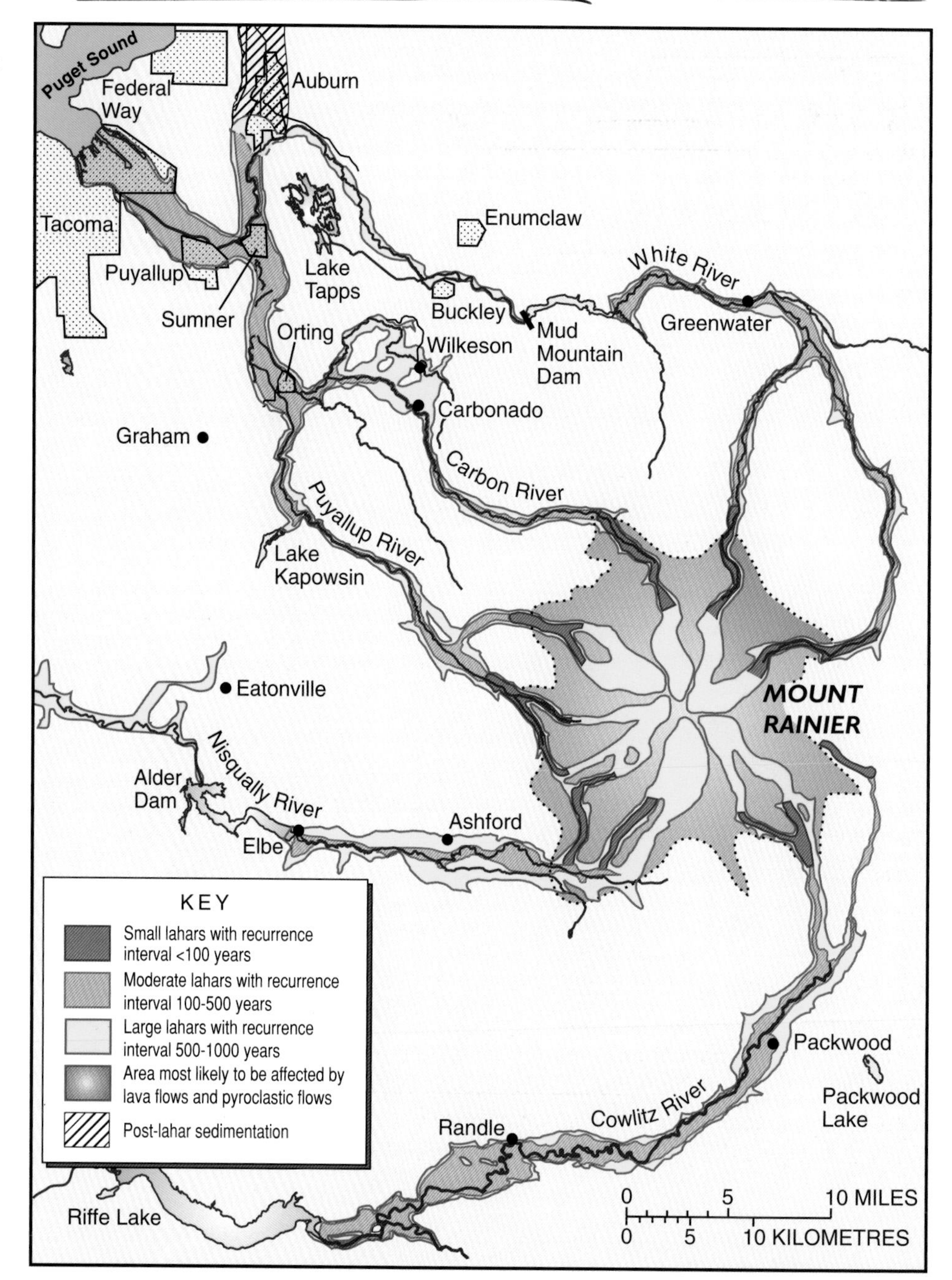

Figure 8.3 Lahar hazard map for the area around Mount Rainier (the same information as in TYVET Figure 8.4).

than airfall) the areas expected to be affected over three different 'recurrence intervals'. Here, recurrence interval means the average time expected between events of a given size. Recurrence intervals are very simply related to annual probability. If a location has a 1 in 1000 (or 0.1%) annual probability of an event (such as the fall of 10 cm or more of ash), this is the same as saying that the recurrence interval is 1000 years.

Question 8.2

Using Figure 8.3, name any towns you can find that are likely to be hit by a lahar:
(a) more than once per century;
(b) approximately every 100–500 years; and
(c) approximately every 500–1000 years.

8.2 Studying the rest of Chapter 8

Now study the rest of Chapter 8. Note that Question 8.3 asks you to produce a table, so you may prefer to do this as you read, rather than returning to do it afterwards.

8.3 Discussion of Chapter 8, pp. 198–214

8.3.1 Crisis management

Do not confuse the volcano Soufrière on Guadeloupe with the Soufriere Hills volcano on Montserrat. They are different volcanoes, although on neighbouring islands. The word *soufrière* is French for 'sulfur mine' and, understandably, is an overused name for volcanoes and volcanic features because of how often sulfur coats the ground around fumaroles (TYVET Plate 13). In fact, the Lesser Antilles island arc includes a third volcano of that name: the volcano Soufrière on St Vincent.

The situation at Nevado del Ruiz in 1985 was mishandled in a different way from that of Soufrière. The next question encourages you to analyse what happened, and to ponder the rights and wrongs.

Question 8.3

In a simple table, summarise the handling of the volcanic crises at Soufrière (Guadeloupe) in 1976 and Nevado del Ruiz in 1985 in terms of: (a) scientific advice; (b) government action; and (c) what happened to the inhabitants of Basse-Terre and Armero.

The IAVCEI videos described in TYVET were made to try to prevent a recurrence of an Armero-type tragedy, and the protocols for communicating scientific advice to the authorities were developed to prevent both extremes of mismanagement. The Pinatubo and Montserrat case studies are examples of more recent volcanic crises that were handled much better, although you can probably think of an aspect that, with the benefit of hindsight, could have been improved.

The times in the MVO report in TYVET are local times, not UT.

Chapter 8 concludes with some examples of active volcanoes that are particularly close to cities. This may be food for thought if you live in, or plan to visit on holiday, such a city.

8.4 Chapter 8 activities and questions

Now do Activities 8.1 and 8.2 and then answer Question 8.4, to conclude your study associated with this chapter.

Activity 8.1 Soufrière, Guadeloupe, 1976

(The estimated time for this activity is 15 minutes.)

The notes for this activity are in the Study Guide.

Activity 8.2 Popocatepetl, Mexico, 2000

(The estimated time for this activity is 25 minutes.)

The notes for this activity are in the Study Guide.

Question 8.4

(You need to have done Activity 8.2 *before* attempting this question, and you will have to draw on your knowledge and experience from elsewhere in the course in order to answer it.)

Explain what you think would have been the likely worst eruption that could have occurred at Popocatepetl in December 2000, which led the authorities to evacuate towns more than 12 km from the volcano. (Write your answer in *150–200 words*.)

Chapter 9
Tectonic earthquakes

Now start reading Chapter 9 and return here when you reach the section 'Measuring earthquakes' (p. 223). If anything confuses you, it may help to refer back to Chapter 2, especially the section 'Plate tectonics, earthquakes and magma generation'. If you find it hard to visualise any of the four types of seismic wave, the animations in Activity 9.1 should clarify them for you.

9.1 Discussion of Chapter 9, pp. 215–23

9.1.1 Faults and earthquakes

Earthquakes (or at least the large, shallow ones capable of doing damage at the surface) happen when the rock mass on one side of a fault moves in a sudden jerk relative to the rock mass on the other side. This occurs when something gives way because too much stress has built up. Gradual deformation occurs elastically (by bending across a broad region) until rupture occurs suddenly on a fault (Figure 9.1). If the reasons behind stick–slip motion were not described clearly enough for you in TYVET, it may help to think of an area before an earthquake as being like a spring-loaded system waiting to go off.

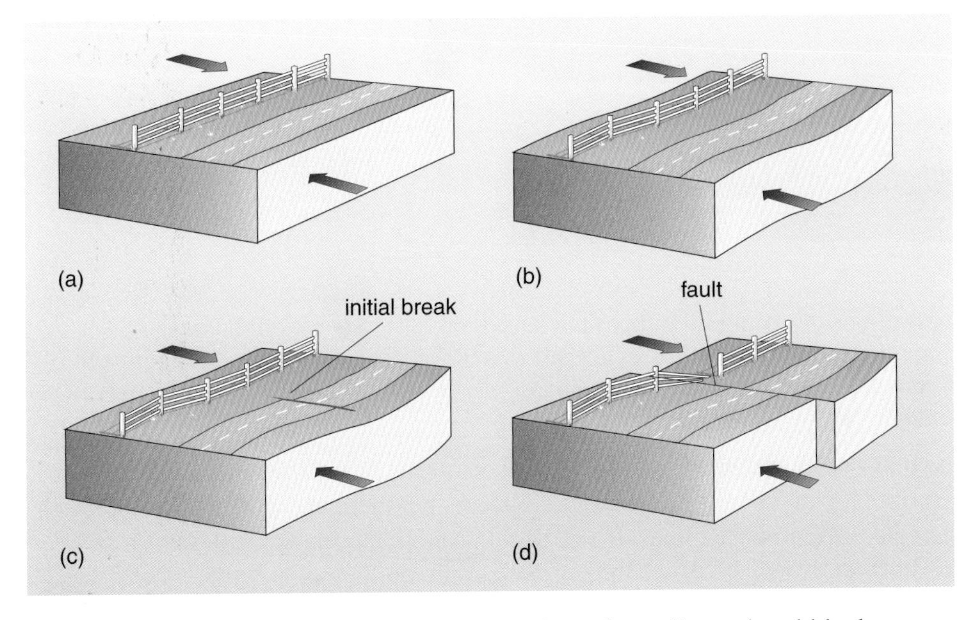

Figure 9.1 How an earthquake happens. These three-dimensional block diagrams show both the surface and the shallow interior. Movement directions are shown by arrows. (a) Part of the Earth where tectonic forces are at work. The road and fence are initially straight. (b) 'Elastic' deformation builds up by bending. (c) The instant of initial rupture. (d) Rupture has propagated along the fault, and elastic deformation has been replaced by brittle fracture. Usually, the fault will now stick in the new position, and deformation will build up elastically again until the next episode of sudden slip. The time between (a) and (b and c) can be hundreds of years, but between (c) and (d) it is just a matter of seconds.

Strictly speaking, the 'straight lines' argument would work only if Earth was flat instead of spherical, but you should be able to see the point.

One reason for stick–slip motion is that faults are not exactly straight lines. They have kinks and, in many cases, the displacement is shared across a set of near-parallel branching faults (which will tend to move at different times). TYVET Figure 9.2 shows this on a large scale, but there is similar complexity down to smaller scales too, and in both plan-view and cross-section. Figure 9.2a here shows a fault exposed in the bank of a stream in northern England. The woman is standing on a prominent bed of rock but, if you try to trace this to the left, you will see that it butts against a browner bed of different characteristics. There must be a fault here and, in fact, if you look closely, you may be able to work out that the fault is not just a single break.

(a)

(b)

Figure 9.2 (a) A fault (hundreds of millions of years old, rather than an active one) exposed in the bank of a stream. The woman is standing on a bed of sandstone, but 3 m to her left this bed is sharply juxtaposed against thinly bedded shales because of a fault that runs vertically away from the camera. (b) Detail of the faulted rock in (a); faults are traced in yellow, the main one being shown by the heaviest line (X–Y).

Figure 9.2b shows an enlargement of the relevant part of the bank, with the faulting picked out. The main fault runs through X and Y, but there are other breaks indicated by the other superimposed lines. If you now consider that faults are not *lines*, as represented on a map, cross-section or photograph, but lumpy *surfaces* where two rock masses meet, it should not surprise you that faults are incapable of smooth, continuous movement. The complexity revealed in Figure 9.2b occurs in three dimensions, not just two, and a fault remains jammed until the stress built up by elastic deformation across the region as a whole has grown sufficiently to unlock the system either by creating a new break or un-jamming an old one.

9.1.2 Focus, epicentre and seismic waves

'Epicentre' is one of those words that journalists tend to misappropriate, writing of something or someone as 'being at the epicentre' of events, as if 'epicentre' means right in the heart of the action. You should realise that this metaphor is not terribly apt because the epicentre of an earthquake is the point on the *surface* directly above the initial rupture, which could be a few hundred kilometres from the focus in the case of a deep earthquake. The focus is where the initial rupture occurs and where most of the seismic energy is released. Figure 9.3 summarises the relationship between epicentre and focus. It is important for you to realise (as pointed out in the first paragraph of TYVET p. 217) that seismic waves are the means by which energy liberated at an earthquake focus is transported to distant places, sometimes violently enough to do considerable damage.

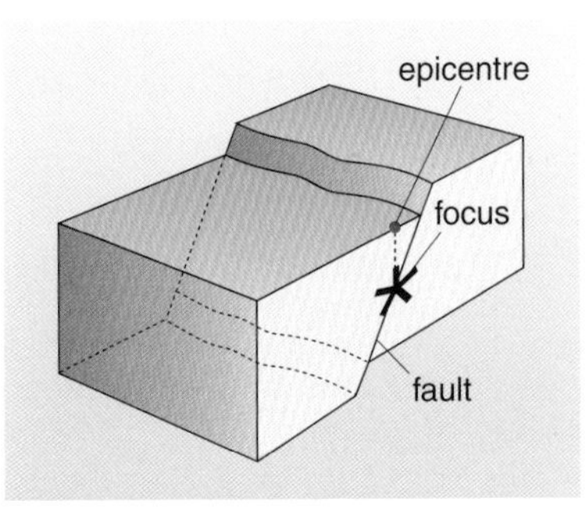

Figure 9.3 The focus and the epicentre of an earthquake.

Now please do Activity 9.1, to consolidate your understanding of seismic waves.

Activity 9.1 Seismic waves and earthquakes

(The estimated time for this activity is 20 minutes.)

The notes for this activity are in the Study Guide.

9.2 Studying the rest of Chapter 9

Now study the rest of Chapter 9 and then return here for the discussion.

9.3 Discussion of Chapter 9, pp. 223–34

9.3.1 Measuring earthquakes

You should be clear about the contrasting nature of the Richter and Mercalli scales. Your answers to some of the questions in this chapter and the next should resolve any misconceptions. Just as for volcanic eruptions, earthquake magnitude is reported on the sort of scale on which an increase of one unit of the scale corresponds to a *tenfold* (i.e. one order of magnitude) increase in some measurable (or calculable) quantity.

You have seen that earthquake magnitude is best determined in different ways, depending on where in the magnitude range it falls. Chapter 9 distinguishes M_L (the original 'Richter scale'), M_W and M_S, but you will find that Chapter 10 simply refers to magnitude, M. This is because the sources of information used (and which you will see on the internet) do not always specify which magnitude scale they are using. The scales are supposed to be roughly equivalent, but if you find the same large earthquake reported as M9.2 in one place and as M8.8 in another, the first is probably M_S and the second M_W, which tends to underestimate magnitudes greater than 8. However, other possible reasons for discrepancies include different scientists selecting data from different seismometers (which cannot be expected to agree exactly), and (for M_W) using different assumptions about the properties of the rock near the source.

How seismometers work was described in Section 7.1.2. In this course, you are not expected to know in detail how the signals detected by globally dispersed seismometers are used in conjunction to deduce the nature and direction of fault motion, nor how the energy released by an earthquake is calculated. However, the basic principles behind using seismometers to characterise the fault motion at an earthquake focus are described in Box 9.1.

Box 9.1 Seismic wave propagation and determining fault motion

Only P- and S-waves originate at an earthquake focus. They radiate away from the focus in all directions (shown as a two-dimensional cross-section in Figure 9.4). Rayleigh waves and Love waves are initiated when energy carried by the P- and S-waves reaches the surface, and they will tend to radiate across the surface away from the epicentre. P-waves are fastest and so are the first to arrive at any seismometer, giving the 'first arrival' trace on a seismogram.

Figure 9.4 shows the position of two seismometers (A and B) on either side of a fault. An earthquake has just happened at the focus, with rock masses on either side of the fault moving in the directions indicated by the arrows. Note that the first manifestation of the P-waves changes on either side of the fault, and is compressional on the side *towards* which fault motion has occurred but is dilational in the opposite direction. In this situation, the first arrival at seismometer A will be compressional and the first arrival at seismometer B will be dilational. Compression results in slight upward ground movement, whereas dilation results in slight downward ground movement; vertical vibrations recorded at A and B as a result of the P-wave will be as shown in the sketched seismogram traces.

■ Which seismometer will detect the earthquake first, and why?

□ Seismometer B will detect it first because this seismometer is closer to the focus.

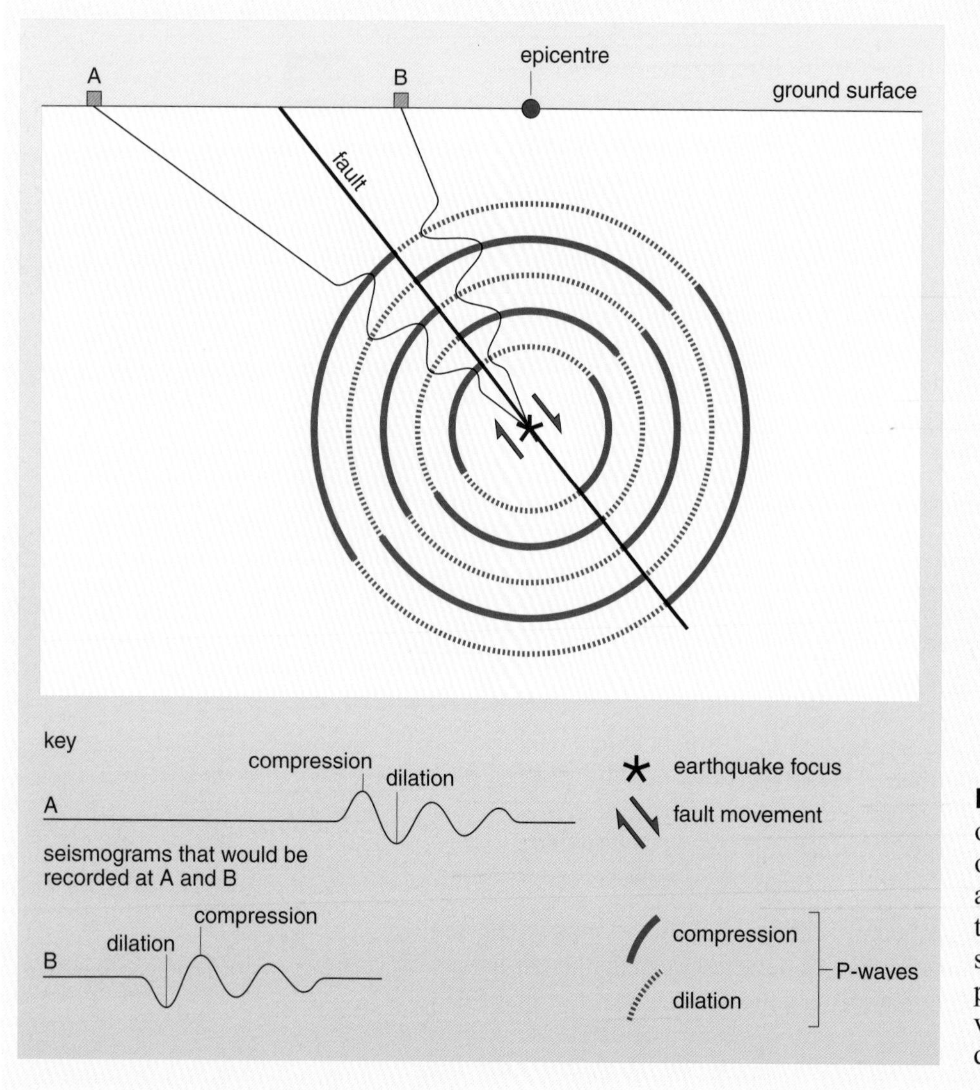

Figure 9.4 Propagation of P-waves from the focus of an earthquake. (At right angles to the fault, where the compression pulse is shown changing to a dilation pulse, the signal would be very weak.) See the text for discussion.

Therefore, it is possible to determine the relative distances of the two seismometers from the focus by comparing the first arrival *times* and the sense of movement at the initial break by comparing the *type* of first arrival (compressional or dilational). By comparing seismograms from numerous seismometers in the Global Seismographic Network, it is possible to infer the orientation of the sort of compression or dilation pattern sketched in Figure 9.4, and hence to determine the nature of fault motion at the focus of a sufficiently strong remote earthquake anywhere in the world, even if the fault itself is unknown.

TYVET Figure 9.7 shows a seismogram from one station of the Global Seismographic Network (GSN). Figure 9.5 here shows the global distribution of GSN seismometers. You will examine information from the GSN in Activity 9.2, at the end of this chapter.

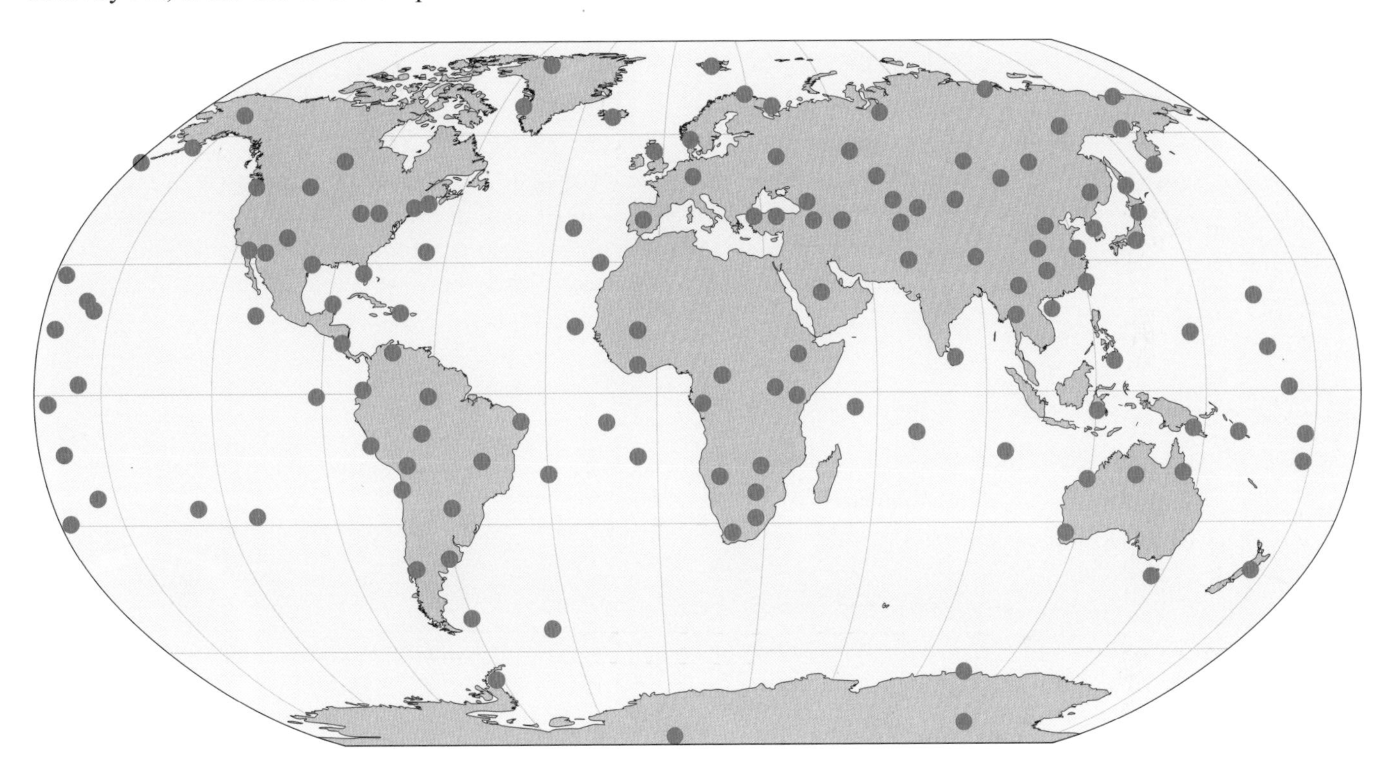

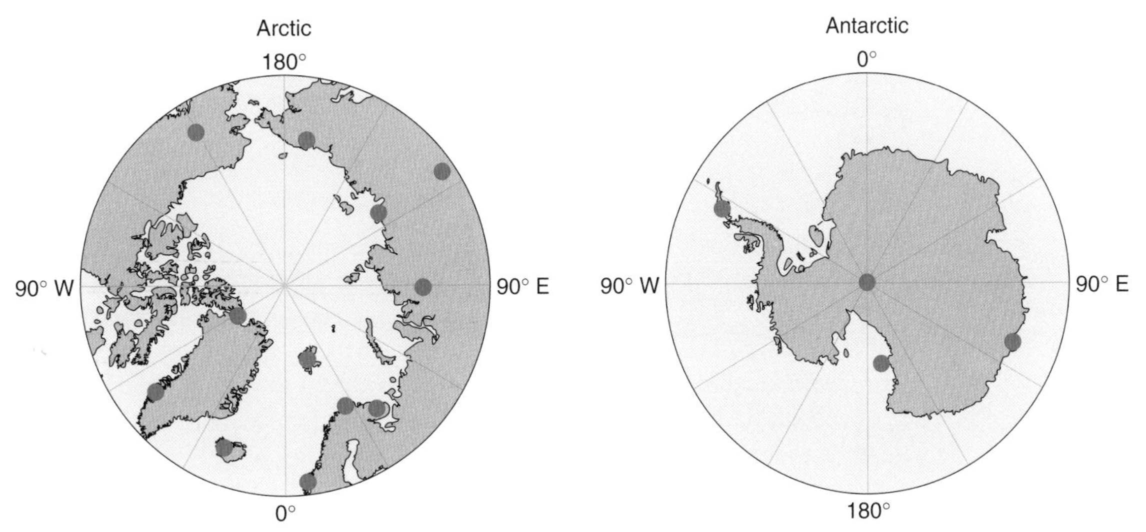

Figure 9.5 Seismometer providing data to the Global Seismographic Network, as of January 2005.

9.3.2 Prediction, warning and prevention

The only comment to make here about the rest of Chapter 9 is that the most useful information on earthquakes can be gathered from a single global array of instruments, whereas the most useful diagnostic information about volcanic activity requires a set of instruments on, or very near, each specific volcano. This makes monitoring earthquakes easier than monitoring volcanoes although, paradoxically, predicting when an earthquake will happen is less straightforward than predicting the eruption of a well-monitored volcano.

9.4 Chapter 9 questions

Now answer Questions 9.1–9.6 and do Activity 9.2, to conclude your study associated with this chapter.

Question 9.1

TYVET Figure 9.4 illustrates three basic types of fault. Which type of fault is responsible for displacing the beds of rock in Figure 9.2? (It will probably help to know that the bed of sandstone the woman is standing on is present to the left of the fault as well, but cannot be seen clearly because there is a lot of soil and grass hiding it.)

Question 9.2

Why is a shallow earthquake more likely to cause serious damage than a deep earthquake? Give two reasons: one concerning *magnitude* and the other *intensity*.

Question 9.3

Why is it less easy for seismic monitoring systems to predict major earthquakes than major eruptions?

Question 9.4

What is the essential difference between earthquake *warning* and earthquake *prediction*? What is the principle behind earthquake warning?

Question 9.5

Imagine that your town is 200 km from the epicentre of an M7 shallow earthquake. Assuming that P-waves travel at 6.0 km/s and surface waves at 3.5 km/s, how soon will (a) P-waves and (b) surface waves arrive? (c) How much sooner will the P-waves arrive than the surface waves? (If you are unfamiliar with km/s meaning kilometres per second, refer to Section 5.1 in the Maths Skills ebook for an example of m/s meaning metres per second.)

Question 9.6

Study TYVET Figure 9.7 carefully. Is the first arrival compressional or dilational?

Activity 9.2 Current and recent earthquakes

(The estimated time for this activity is 15 minutes.)

The notes for this activity are in the Study Guide.

Chapter 10
Living with earthquakes

Now read Chapter 10, which describes the nature and consequences of several notable earthquakes, followed by a discussion of what can be done to reduce the vulnerability of people and infrastructure to the effects of earthquakes.

10.1 Discussion of Chapter 10

10.1.1 Notable earthquakes

You may remember some of the more recent examples from this chapter being reported on the news. You may even have relatives or friends who were directly affected. Sadly, there is likely to have been another newsworthy earthquake requiring an international relief effort by the time you study this course.

There is little to add to the discussion of the 'case studies' of particular earthquakes in this chapter, other than to show a few more illustrations of their effects (Figures 10.1 and 10.2). These are all accessible online (along with hundreds of others) from the USGS Earthquake Hazards Program website, which was introduced in Activity 9.2, but it may be helpful and convenient for you see some here.

Figure 10.1 (a) Mexico City, 1985: this view may appear normal at first sight, but the top three stories of the left-hand wing of the Continental Hotel have collapsed, as have the upper stories of the building in the background.
(b) Proof that earthquakes don't open up chasms down to the bowels of the Earth. This residential street was cut by a fault rupture during the 1989 Lomo Prieta earthquake but, at less than 2 metres deep, it is filled by fragmented rubble firm enough to stand on.

(a)

(b)

(c)

Figure 10.2 Northridge earthquake damage, 1994: (a) emergency workers checking damaged buildings; (b) part of an elevated freeway brought down by the earthquake; (c) although these buildings appear to have stood up well, more than enough masonry has been shaken onto the street to kill passers-by.

10.1.2 Fatalities from earthquakes and volcanoes

By now it should be apparent that single earthquakes have been known to kill hundreds of thousands of people. A death toll of a few millions from one earthquake is not out of the question but that would seem to be about the upper limit.

It is considerably rarer for a volcanic eruption to take as many as ten thousand lives than it is for an earthquake to do so. However, the largest eruptions could devastate the greater part of an area such as the USA and even lead to *billions* of deaths if the effects on climate are as bad as some scientists fear. Such events are infrequent but the geological record provides clear evidence that they have happened in the past.

Question 10.1

Which is the worse threat to humanity: earthquakes or volcanoes? Consider this carefully, and then write an account *of about 200–300 words*, justifying your reasoning.

The rest of Chapter 10 takes a more positive stance, and considers 'earthquake proofing' and preparedness as ways to reduce vulnerability to earthquake hazard.

10.1.3 Earthquake proofing

The main message from this section of Chapter 10 is that there are many ways to make buildings and other engineered structures less vulnerable to earthquakes. In many parts of the world where large earthquakes are frequent, 'earthquake proofing' is required by official building codes. Unfortunately, it is common in many countries for such codes to be flouted, for a variety of reasons mostly to do with 'saving' money. This seems to be all too prevalent where schools are concerned.

There are two issues concerning how buildings and the ground react to seismic waves (particularly the surface waves that do the damage) that may benefit from further explanation. These are *resonance* and *liquefaction*. The first concerns a building shaking 'in tune' with the motion of the ground. Any object, including a building, has a natural frequency at which it vibrates most readily. One example from everyday life is a domestic washing machine: when its spin drier is working at normal speed, a properly designed washing machine will experience very little vibration. However, while the spinning drum is slowing down after the spin drier has completed its cycle, there is usually a brief time when the rate of spin coincides with the natural frequency of vibration of the washing-machine cabinet, and for a few seconds the whole machine will resonate. The amount of shaking and associated noise increase temporarily, until the rate of spin drops below what is necessary to excite this 'resonant vibration'.

In an earthquake, the equivalent is the ground shaking at the right frequency to make a building resonate, which depends mostly on the height of the building. If the ground shaking is faster than the building can respond to, objects within – such as furniture – will rattle around, but the shape of the building will not distort. However, ground shaking with a period of a few seconds is liable to set a multistorey building swaying in an exaggerated fashion at the same rate, and this is when there is the greatest danger of collapse. Slower ground shaking will result in the entire building moving in unison with the ground, with much less likelihood of damage.

■ If the period of ground shaking (meaning the time it takes to sway to and fro) is 4.0 seconds, what is the frequency of this motion?

□ Using the relationship given in Box 7.1, frequency = 1/period, which in this case = 1/(4.0 seconds) = 0.25 per second = 0.25 hertz.

The Marquês de Pombal's innovative (I nearly wrote 'ground breaking'!) experiments in which he had soldiers march around scale models of proposed buildings for the new Lisbon were flawed, unless he realised that scale models have faster resonant frequencies than full-sized buildings and adjusted the rate of the marching footfalls to simulate the effect of seismic ground shaking accordingly.

To avoid shaking down a bridge by means of exciting a resonant vibration, columns of troops are not allowed to march in step while they cross. In the UK in 2000 the Millennium Bridge, a new 330 m steel footbridge over the River Thames in London, was hurriedly closed because the footfalls of pedestrians set it swaying in resonance. It was reopened two years later, fitted with various devices to 'damp out' this motion. Similar shock absorbers are mentioned in Chapter 10 in the context of specially engineered high-rise buildings, but they are now marketed for wooden-framed homes, as you will see if you search for the terms 'earthquake' and 'shock absorber' on the internet.

Liquefaction concerns the effect of seismic waves on the ground itself. It occurs in ground containing a layer of soil that is saturated (or nearly so) by water between the grains. Shaking of the ground at particular frequencies causes the saturated layer to lose its strength and stiffness, so that buildings on top of it simply sink into it (see Box 10.1 if you find it hard to imagine this). TYVET Figure 10.7 shows a notable Japanese example, and Figure 10.3a here shows a different outcome of liquefaction in the Marina District of San Francisco. The land here had been created by filling a lagoon with dune sand and building rubble from the great earthquake of 1906. The resulting soil was both loosely consolidated and water-saturated, leading to both amplified shaking and liquefaction during the 1989 Loma Prieta earthquake. Figure 10.3b shows how little of the San Fernando reservoir dam escaped collapse because of liquefaction during the 1971 Los Angeles earthquake.

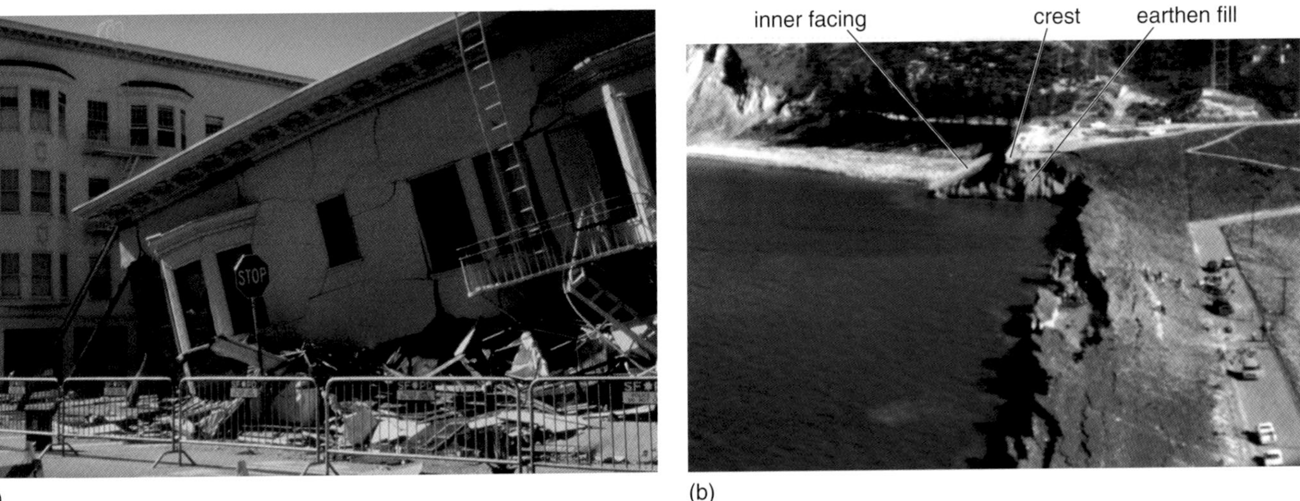

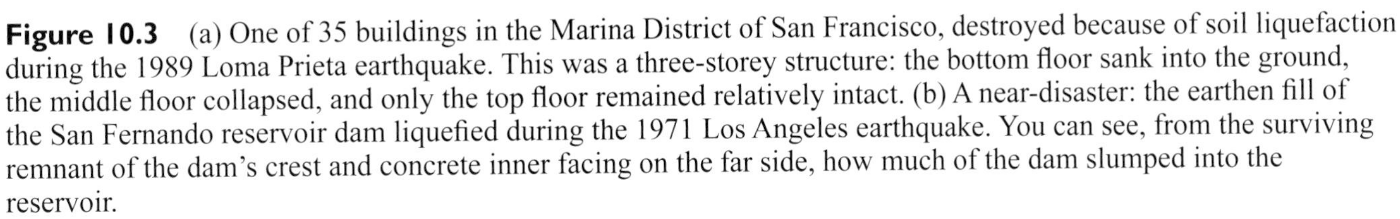

Figure 10.3 (a) One of 35 buildings in the Marina District of San Francisco, destroyed because of soil liquefaction during the 1989 Loma Prieta earthquake. This was a three-storey structure: the bottom floor sank into the ground, the middle floor collapsed, and only the top floor remained relatively intact. (b) A near-disaster: the earthen fill of the San Fernando reservoir dam liquefied during the 1971 Los Angeles earthquake. You can see, from the surviving remnant of the dam's crest and concrete inner facing on the far side, how much of the dam slumped into the reservoir.

Box 10.1 Do-it-yourself liquefaction

If you have ever stood barefoot on the wet sand of a beach and wiggled your toes, or generally jiggled your weight around, it does not take much wiggling or jiggling before the sand suddenly liquefies and your feet sink several centimetres into it. Many shellfish, such as molluscs and crabs, take advantage of this phenomenon to bury themselves, by agitating the wet sand below them rather than digging to make a hole.

10.1.4 Earthquake preparedness

Are *you* prepared for an earthquake? I am pretty sure that my largely stone-built house in Northamptonshire, parts of which are 200 years old, would not stand up to shaking measuring VII or VIII on the Mercalli scale. However, at least I know what to do in an earthquake, as you should by now, if you remember the advice from the Los Angeles telephone directory. Similar advice is repeated in many places on the internet, several of which can be found through the 'Preparedness and Response' link on the 'About Earthquakes' page of the USGS Earthquake Hazards Program website, which you visited in Activity 9.2.

I have experienced mild earthquakes during trips to Los Angeles and Chile, and once was woken up by one at home, which you will examine in Activity 10.2. Before that, do Activity 10.1, where you will see a seismic hazard map, but first read Box 10.2, which explains seismic hazard maps.

Box 10.2 Seismic hazard maps

Seismic hazard maps are analogous to the volcanic airfall hazard maps which you saw in Chapter 8. They portray the likelihood of ground shaking of a certain strength in future earthquakes. They are used as part of the decision-making process when defining

(1) standards of earthquake 'proofing' required for buildings and (2) the importance of earthquake-specific hazard awareness among the public and the emergency services in a particular region. Figure 10.4 shows the factors that need to be taken into consideration. In (a) the locations of the earthquakes that have caused major damage are shown. However, this overlooks smaller earthquakes that give a fuller picture of where future damaging earthquakes may happen. These are shown schematically in (b) but this lacks information on how strong the resulting ground motion tends to be, so version (c) factors in the historically measured maximum shaking. Allowance is also needed for the fact that earthquakes are more common in some areas than others, which leads to (d).

Even Figure 10.4d is not adequate, because geological evidence about prehistoric earthquakes should also be considered, to give the fullest possible basis for predictions. The final result, taking everything into account, is shown in Figure 10.5. This is a contoured map of seismic hazard, showing areas where, during a 50-year period, the maximum ground acceleration (the strength of the shaking) has a 10% or higher chance of exceeding the values indicated on the scale. Acceleration in this case is measured as '% g', meaning a percentage of what is felt because of the Earth's gravity. In other words, during upward acceleration of 20% g, your weight would feel 120% (100% + 20%) of its usual value, whereas during downward acceleration of 20% g, your weight would feel only 80% (100% – 20%) of its usual value. (You might have experienced a momentary feeling of reduced weight when a car you were travelling in went too fast over a hump-backed bridge.)

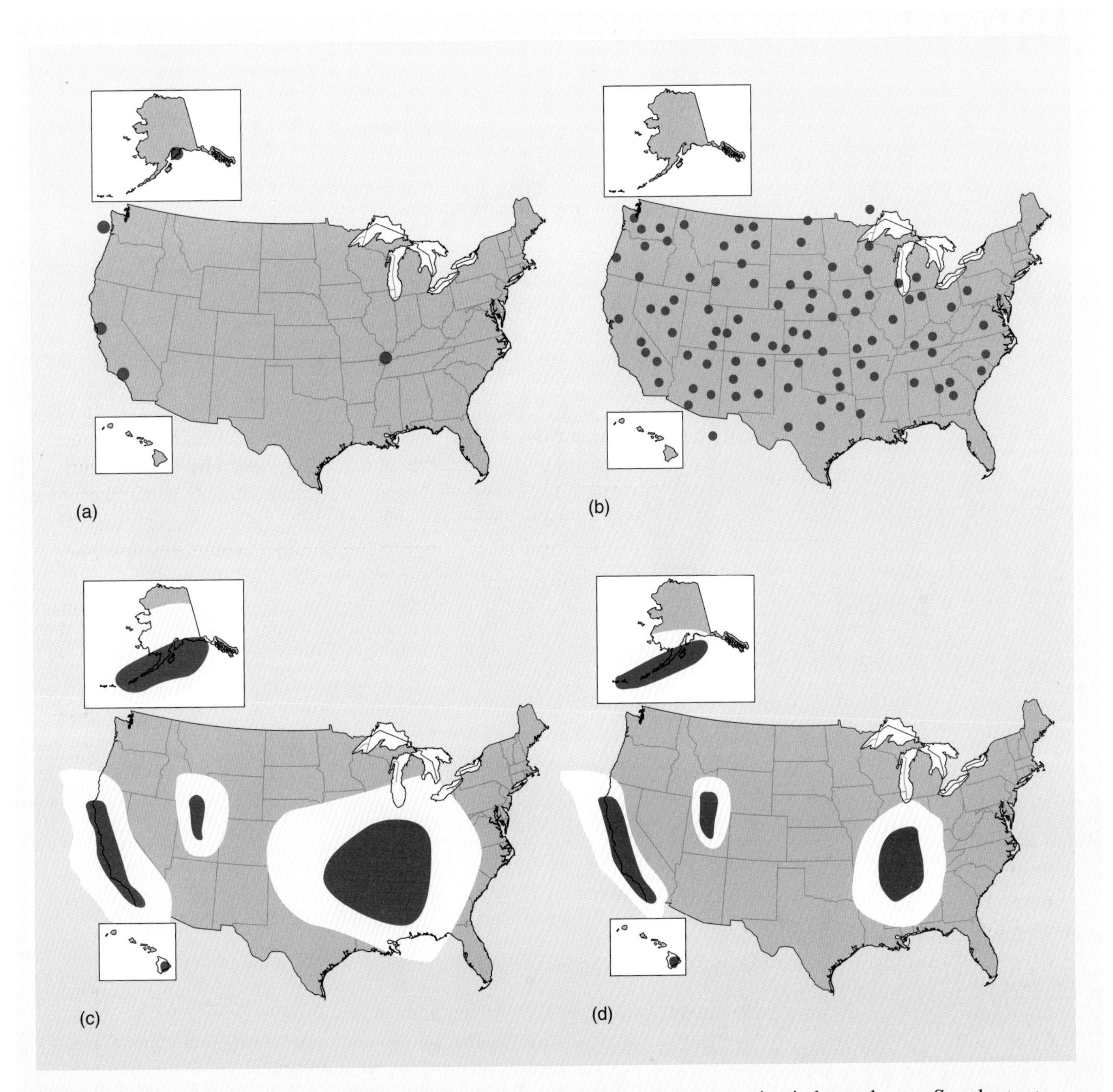

Figure 10.4 Schematic illustrations of the steps necessary to construct a seismic hazard map. See the text of Box 10.2 for discussion.

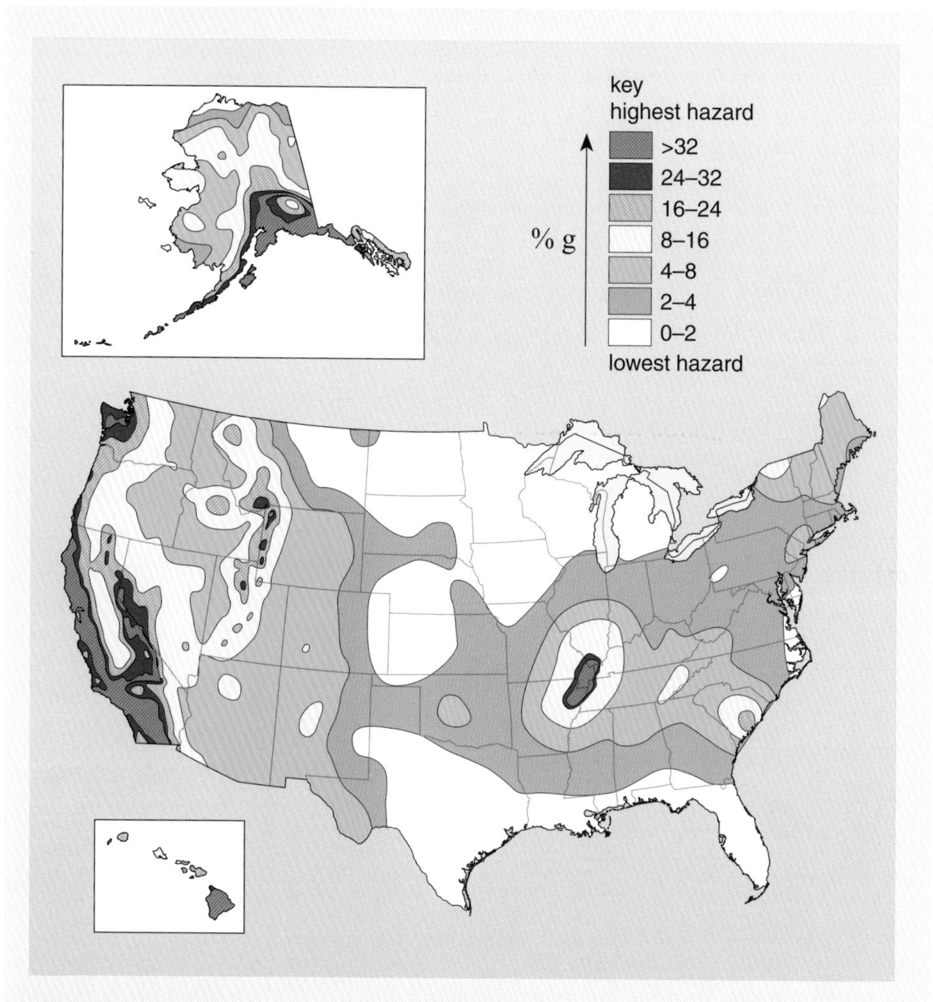

Figure 10.5 Completed seismic hazard map for the USA, showing (by means of contours) the peak ground shaking that has a 10% probability of being exceeded within 50 years.

10.2 Chapter 10 questions

Now answer Questions 10.2–10.4 and do Activities 10.1 and 10.2, to conclude your study associated with this chapter.

Question 10.2

Look carefully at the damage to the Continental Hotel in Figure 10.1a. Bearing in mind what you know about the conditions of this particular earthquake, why did this happen?

Question 10.3

List as many ways as you can think of to make a building 'earthquake proof'.

Question 10.4

Imagine that you are in a house, alone, reading this book at the dining-room table. Suddenly the room starts to shake violently. It is an earthquake. What should you do immediately, and why?

Question 10.5

The USA seismic hazard map in Figure 10.5, unsurprisingly, shows relatively high hazard near the plate boundary on the Pacific coast, and on the volcanically active Big Island of Hawaii. However, there is a small region of relatively high hazard on the Atlantic coast, and a larger area of somewhat higher hazard centred on part of the Mississippi river valley. How do these two 'anomalies' relate to what you read about in Chapter 10?

Activity 10.1 Shake intensity and hazard maps

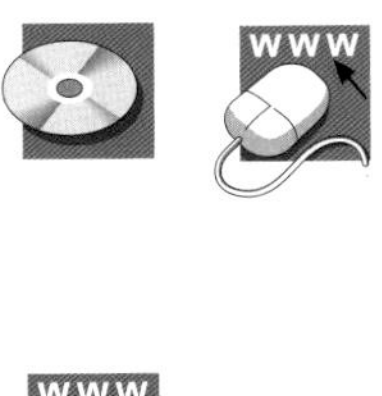

(The estimated time for this activity is 30 minutes.)

The notes for this activity are in the Study Guide.

Activity 10.2 Earthquakes in the British Isles

(The estimated time for this activity is 10 minutes.)

The notes for this activity are in the Study Guide.

Chapter 11 Tsunamis

Authors are advised not to make general assumptions about their students' experience when preparing course materials, to avoid anyone feeling overlooked or excluded. However, I shall break that rule here by stating that you will have some memory of the tragic unfolding news of the Indian Ocean tsunami of 26 December 2004 (Figure 11.1). It touched us all in one way or another.

Now read Chapter 11, which brings the course to a close with a discussion of this and other tsunamis resulting from a variety of trigger mechanisms. Then return to this Study Book for the final activities and questions.

Figure 11.1 Headline stories in British newspapers on 27 December (the two on the left), 29 December (top right) and 30 December (bottom right) 2004.

11.1 Discussion of Chapter 11

11.1.1 Tsunami triggers and propagation

The example of ripples from a pebble thrown into a lake in Chapter 11 is a good analogy for how tsunami waves occur in a series (rather than a single wave) radiating away from the source of the disturbance. However, it can be hard to picture how an earthquake below the sea floor can cause potentially devastating waves on the sea surface. The first animation in Activity 11.1 attempts to clarify this, and others show how the Indian Ocean tsunami in 2004 was propagated. Please do this activity as soon as it is convenient.

Activity 11.1 Tsunami animations

(The estimated time for this activity is 10 minutes.)

The notes for this activity are in the Study Guide.

As you saw in the second animation in Activity 11.1, the slowing down of waves as they move across shallower water is associated with the wave profile becoming steeper and height often amplified. This can increase the run-up to lethal proportions.

11.1.2 Historic seismogenic tsunamis

Several lethal tsunamis caused by earthquakes were described here, with at least one example from each of the major oceans. Please remember that tsunamis at sea generally do not take the form of giant breaking waves such as that in the famous and iconic Japanese woodblock print reproduced on the cover of this book, which is part of a series entitled *Thirty Six Views of Mount Fuji*. It is not known whether the artist (Katsushika Hokusai 1760–1849) intended to portray a tsunami, or simply a storm wave. Tsunamis do not always break like that even when they reach shallow water.

Seismogenic tsunamis are considerably more common in the Pacific Ocean than in either the Indian or the Atlantic Oceans.

Question 11.1

Why are seismogenic tsunamis more common in the Pacific Ocean? It may help if you refer to Figure 2.3.

The Okushiri tsunami in 1993 is an interesting example of waves from a locally triggered tsunami having a run-up of as much as 30 m over a vulnerable, exposed peninsula. You can see an animation of this event and real video of the 2004 Indian Ocean tsunami in Activity 11.2, which you should do as soon as it is convenient.

Activity 11.2 Tsunami inundation

(The estimated time for this activity is 20 minutes.)

The notes for this activity are in the Study Guide.

One reason why wave crests become bent when waves interact with shorelines is that the speed of travel is less in shallower water, as you saw in Activity 11.1. Also, a wave passing through a channel between two islands will 'radiate' out into the sheltered water beyond. Both these effects can be discerned in Figure 11.2, which shows maps of calculated travel time for tsunami waves originating from specific sources. Note that these show simply the time for the first wave to arrive. There is no indication of the likely *height* of the waves, although generally speaking this will decrease with increasing distance from the source. In the case of the 1755 Lisbon tsunami, you can see from the bunching up of the travel-time contours that the wave speed decreased dramatically when it passed onto the shallow water of the continental shelf west of the British Isles. In such a situation, it is a matter of some complexity whether the waves would become steeper (and thus more dangerous) or whether sufficient energy would be absorbed or reflected by the edge of the shelf to undo this effect.

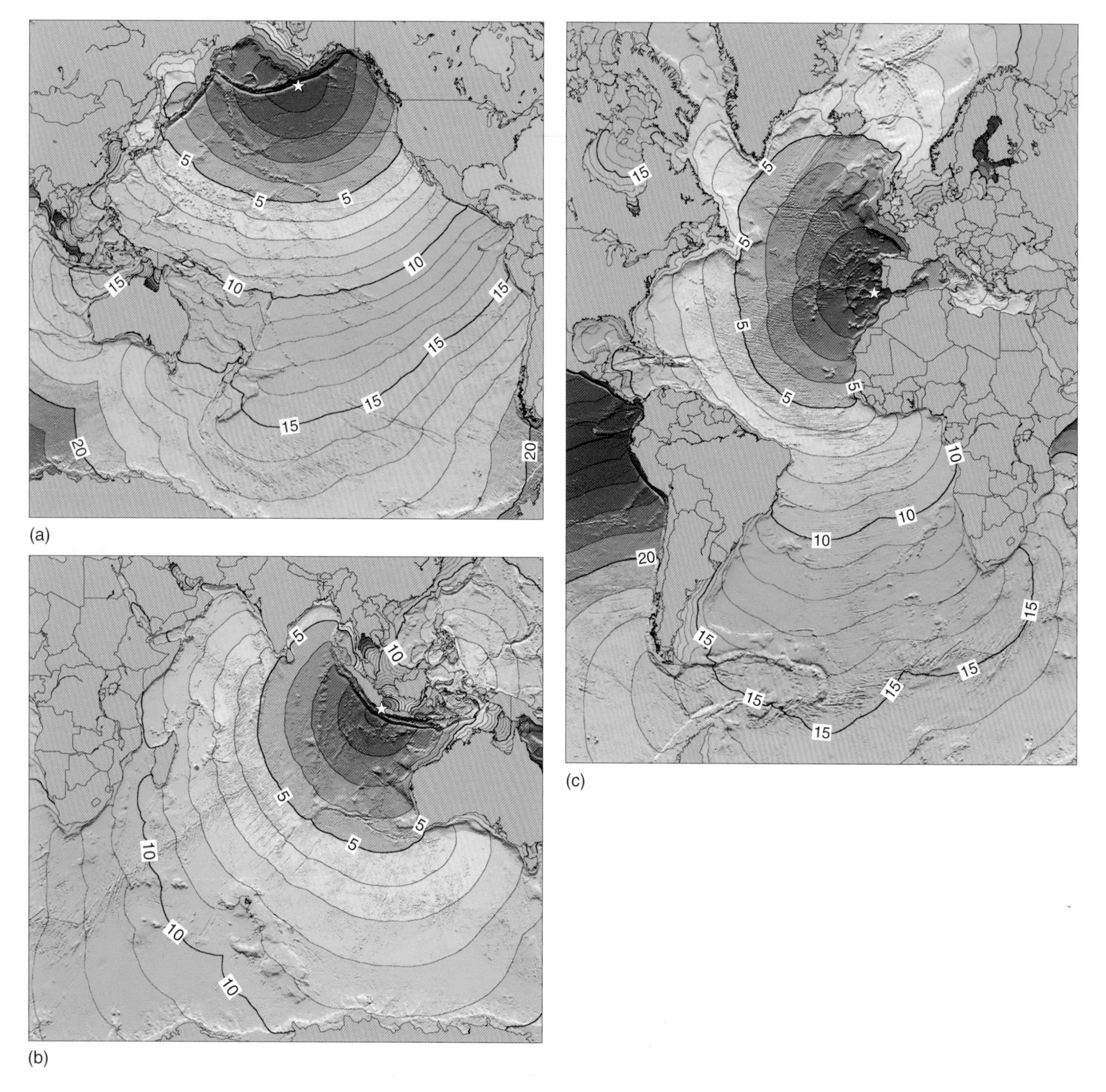

Figure 11.2 Calculated first-arrival travel time for three historic tsunamis: (a) the 1946 Aleutian tsunami; (b) the 1883 Krakatau volcanogenic tsunami; (c) the 1755 Lisbon tsunami. (Contours are travel time in hours.)

There are some pictures in TYVET of the devastation caused by the Indian Ocean tsunami in 2004. There are two more here in Figure 11.3. There are hundreds more available on the internet, which are not hard to find. You have also seen some of the best video of this event in Activity 11.2.

(a) (b)

Figure 11.3 (a) View from a helicopter of the west coast of Aceh province, northern Sumatra after the tsunami on 24 December 2004. Note the near-total devastation of the coastal plain and signs of run-up far inland in the distant valley. (b) Closer view of the tsunami aftermath in the same region as (a). On the left, survivors queue up to receive aid.

11.1.3 Tsunami warnings, preparedness and protection

It took several days for the scale of the disaster caused by the Indian Ocean tsunami in 2004 to become apparent. Figure 11.1 shows casualty estimates in *The Guardian* newspaper on 27, 29 and 30 December rising from 'Giant waves kill thousands' to 'Number killed nears 60 000' to 'Death toll could reach 100 000' – which is still less than half the finally accepted figure. The tragedy exposed serious weaknesses in both preparedness and warning systems for a tsunami in the Indian Ocean, which unfortunately seem not to have been learned on Java where 550 people died as a result of a tsunami less than two years later.

Chapter 11 explains that, although earthquakes are easy to detect and well monitored, seismic data alone cannot determine whether the quake has triggered a significant tsunami. Pressure sensors on the ocean floor are the only sure way to detect the passage of tsunami waves in the deep ocean. They can do this because the pressure measured by a sensor on the ocean floor depends on the amount of water above it, so pressure is higher when a wave crest passes and lower when a wave trough passes. Figures 11.4–11.6 illustrate the DART system and how it functions. Activity 11.3 (at the end of this section) takes you to a website where you can find out more. Warnings are issued on the basis of detection of a tsunami by DART, but recommendations for coastal evacuation depend also on computer models of the expected run-up when such waves reach the shore.

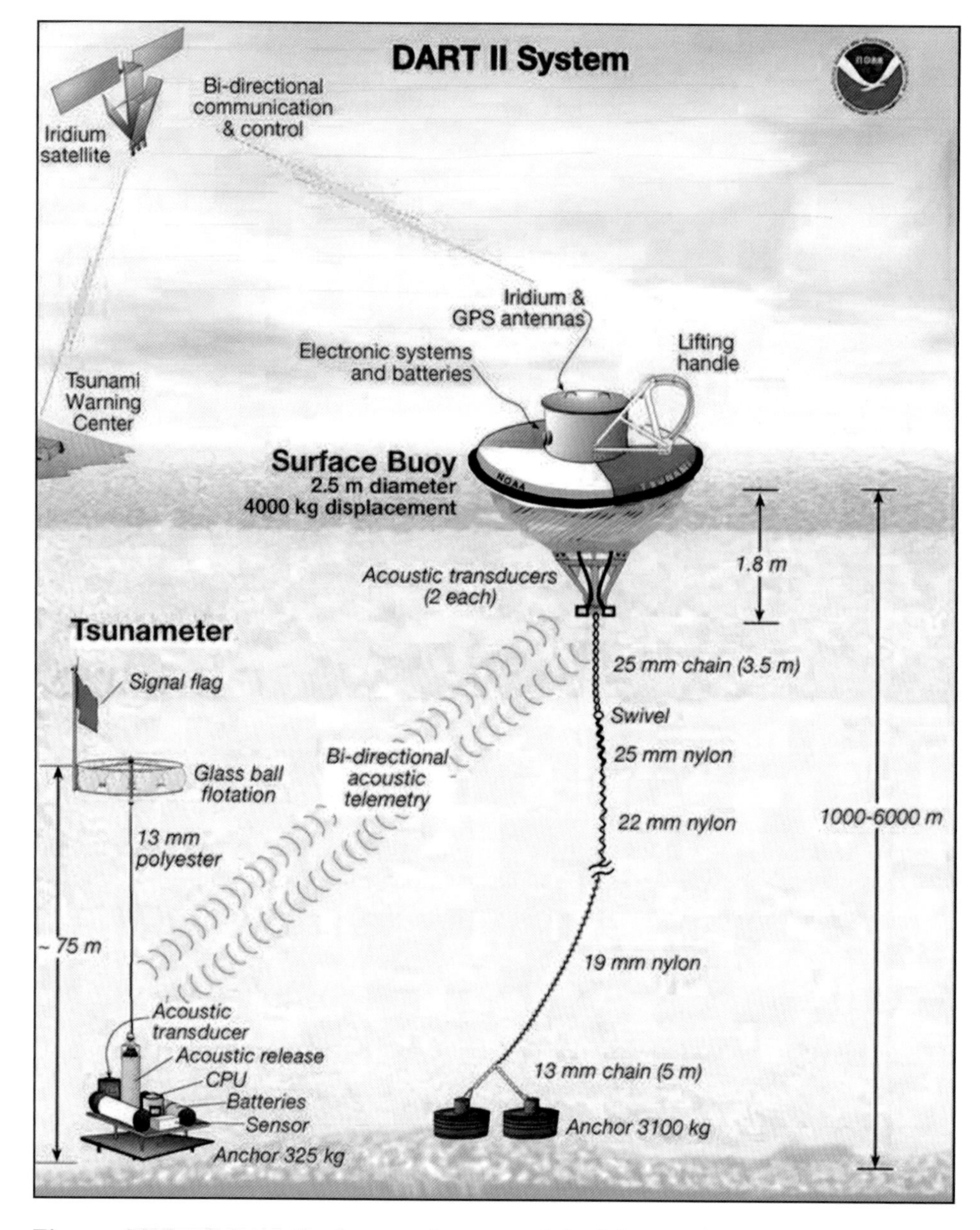

Figure 11.4 Schematic diagram (not to scale) of the components of a DART station: the 'tsunameter' includes a bottom pressure recorder which sits on the ocean floor and communicates acoustically with a moored surface buoy. The buoy communicates to shore through a satellite radio link.

Figure 11.5 (a) A DART bottom pressure recorder ready to be deployed. The small metallic cylinder (A) is the titanium case housing the electronics for the pressure sensor; the white tubes (B) contain batteries; the acoustic communications are in the orange case (C); and the yellow cylinder (D) is an acoustically triggered release to detach the whole device from its anchor so it can float back to the surface for repair or refurbishment. (b) A DART buoy about to be deployed.

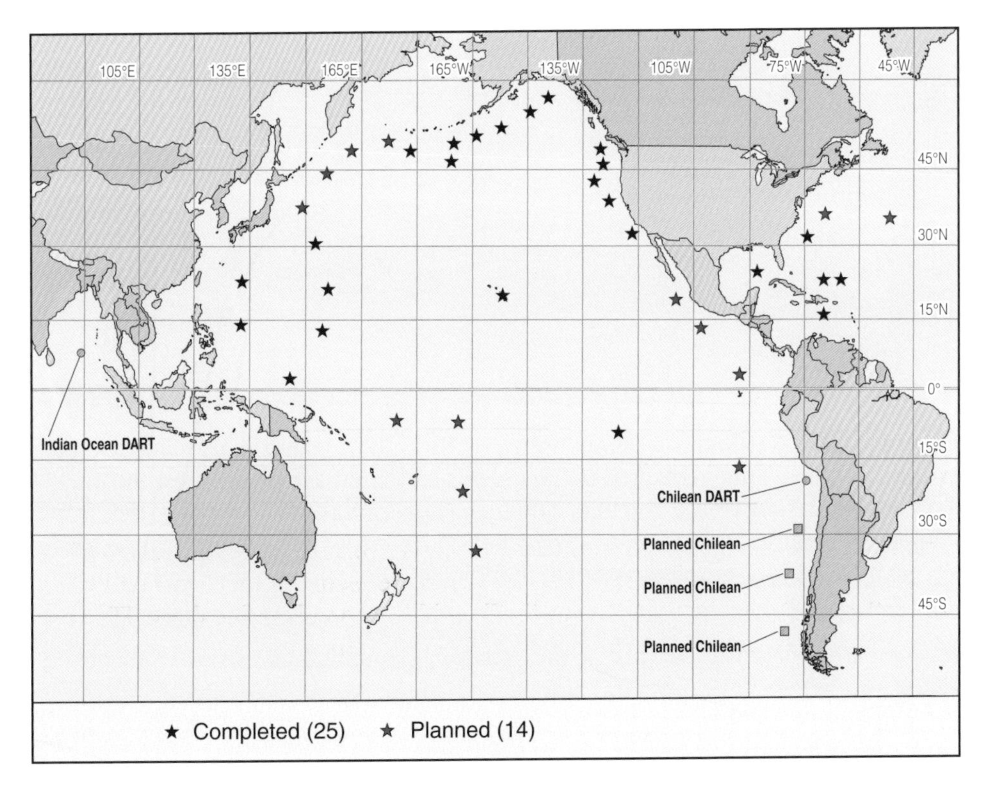

Figure 11.6 Map of the existing and planned DART system in March 2007.

The best ways to save lives are likely to be warnings distributed from the DART system, and self-evacuation from vulnerable coasts in the case of a felt-earthquake as urged in the UNESCO notice reproduced in TYVET (pp. 271–2). The awareness of local people and tourists can be raised by warning signs and signposting evacuation routes (Figure 11.7). As for reducing the vulnerability of buildings to the hazard, Japanese-style offshore tsunami walls are feasible only in front of high-value, high-risk shorelines. There appears to be no allowance for tsunamis in the British Isles because the annual hazard is perceived to be too slight to worry about.

Figure 11.7 A tsunami warning notice on Stromboli Island, Italy. This relates primarily to tsunamis generated by landslides on the unstable ash slope forming the northwest flank of the volcano. The map shows areas of the town at risk from inundation (orange) and pedestrian evacuation routes, which are marked on the streets by orange or green directional markers as illustrated on the larger notice.

As soon as it is convenient, please do Activity 11.3, which takes you to a website acting as a gateway for news and information about tsunamis.

Activity 11.3 Tsunami websites

(The estimated time for this activity is 30 minutes.)

The notes for this activity are in the Study Guide, except for Figures 11.8 and 11.9.

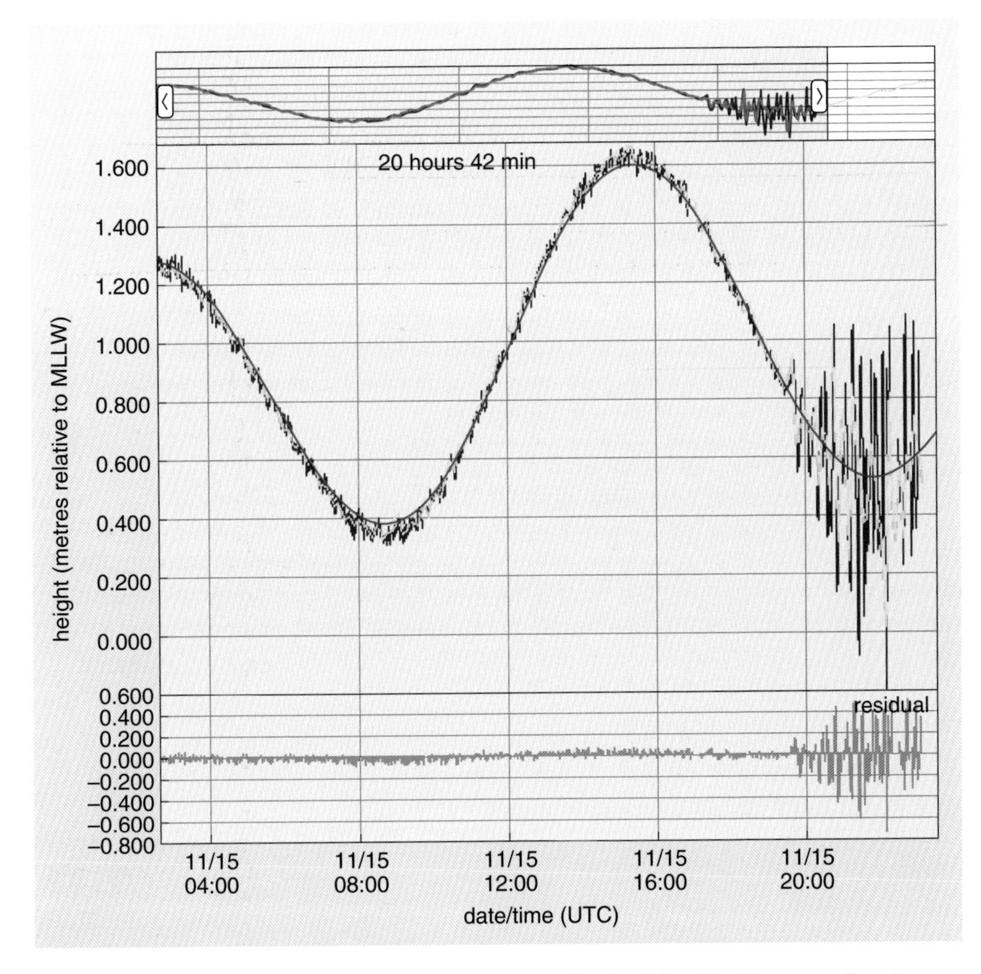

Figure 11.8 Tide gauge data showing the arrival of the Kuril tsunami at Arena Cove, California on 15 November 2006. For use in Activity 11.3. (MLLW stands for 'mean lower low water' and is the average level of the lowest low water each day. It is a standard datum against which to record tides.)

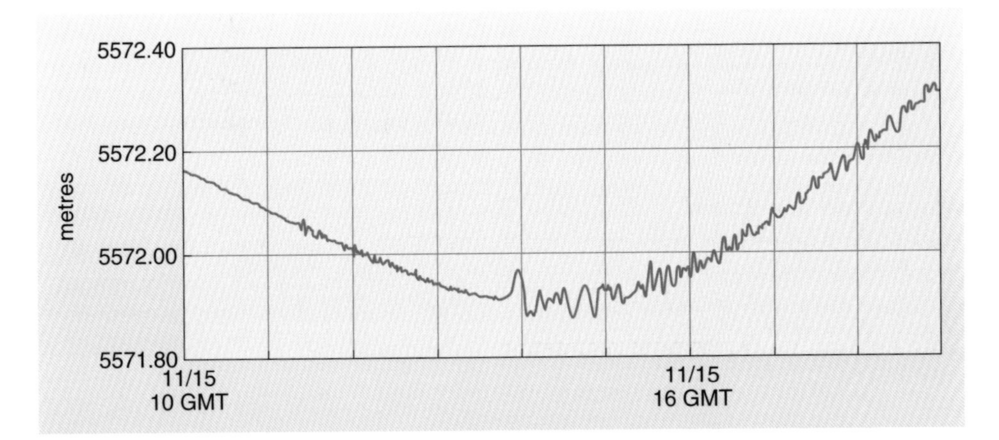

Figure 11.9 DART record from a buoy south of the Aleutian Islands, Alaska, showing the water column height above station 46413, recording the 15 November 2006 Kuril tsunami. For use in Activity 11.3 and Question 11.4.

11.1.4 Landslide and impact tsunamis

The final two sections of Chapter 11 complete the tsunami story. There is nothing to add here about landslide tsunamis. It is easy to find the two examples in TYVET on the internet if you want to know more about them.

Impact tsunamis are a frightening but rare hazard, and, as mentioned in Chapter 11, the tsunami itself is not necessarily the worst of the consequences of an impact on the ocean. Surveys to locate impact craters on the ocean floor continue, and so does the debate over the correct interpretation of such structures and the associated 'tsunami' deposits. You would search the Dynamic Earth map in Activity 2.2 in vain for the controversial Eltanin crater, although it does mark the impact sites for Chicxulub and Chesapeake Bay.

11.2 Chapter 11 questions

Now answer Questions 11.2–11.5, to conclude your study associated with this chapter and, indeed, of the course. I hope you enjoyed it and that you are still sufficiently interested to follow future events on some of the websites you have visited. Finally, please don't forget to submit your End of Course Assessment!

Question 11.2

Give two reasons why the first sign of a tsunami arriving is often 'drawback' (that is, the sea withdraws from the shore).

Question 11.3

Name and describe, *in one sentence each*, *four* different ways in which tsunamis can be generated in the oceans.

Question 11.4

At the DART station providing the record in Figure 11.9, did the first tsunami wave arrive as a crest or a trough, and what was happening to the tidal height at this time?

Question 11.5

Imagine that the nucleus of a comet breaks apart into two fragments, each about 200 m across, shortly before impact on Earth. One fragment strikes the Atlantic Ocean, where the water is 4 km deep, and the other strikes the North Sea, where the water is 80 m deep. Write an account of *150–200 words* to explain whether either of these events is liable to cause a powerful tsunami.

Answers to questions

Further comments on the answers are given in square brackets [...].

Question 1.1

The answer to this is in Section 1.2 of this Study Book, which tells you that exceptional volcanoes can be active for as long as 2–3 million years. [Incidentally, the meaning of 'active' volcano is a rather complex issue. You will find a discussion of this at the end of TYVET Chapter 3, pp. 62–4.]

Question 1.2

(c) Edinburgh because the volcanic rocks there are very old (about 340 million years).

Question 1.3

TYVET p. 3 tells you that the tsunami caused by this eruption killed more people than the eruption itself. [You will learn more about this in TYVET Chapter 5.]

Question 2.1

Molten rock containing crystals and/or bubbles is correctly described as 'magma', whereas 'melt' refers only to the liquid part of a magma. 'Lava' describes magma (molten rock) when it has found its way to the Earth's surface. [You will learn later in Chapter 2 that 'lava' is also used to refer to rock formed by solidification of molten lava.]

Question 2.2

TYVET Table 2.1 shows that continental crust has on average 62% silica, whereas oceanic crust has 49% and the mantle 45% silica.

Question 2.3

(a) The crust (whether oceanic or continental) plus the uppermost part of the mantle immediately below the crust form a single mechanical layer, which is the lithosphere.

(b) The lithosphere is rigid. All of the mantle below the lithosphere is weaker, and undergoes solid-state convection, flowing at a few centimetres per year. The uppermost part of the convecting mantle (known as the asthenosphere) may have a trace (a few per cent) of melt within it, but effectively it is still a solid.

(c) TYVET Figure 2.2 labels the junction as 'Moho'. [This term is used by geologists to denote the base of the crust. It is short for Mohorovičić Discontinuity, named after Andrija Mohorovičić (1857–1936), a Croatian seismologist (earthquake scientist) who was the first to identify it.]

Question 2.4

I would hope that you wrote something along the following lines (curiously, only in the final example is the melting caused by a rise in temperature of the source material).

- Upwelling of mantle below a constructive plate boundary leads to partial melting because of decompression of the upwelling material (decompression melting).
- Water escaping upwards from a subducting slab at a destructive plate boundary lowers the melting temperature of the rock into which it passes, and so causes partial melting in the mantle or crust of the overlying plate (hydration melting).
- At a destructive plate boundary the subducting plate eventually reaches depths at which heat conducted into it from the warm asthenosphere makes it sufficiently hot to begin to melt.

Question 2.5

Both figures call this the Nazca Plate. Note that this underlies only a small part of the whole of the Pacific Ocean basin.

Question 2.6

As TYVET Figure 2.6 shows, earthquakes are concentrated near the upper edge of a subducting plate. The Nazca Plate is subducting eastwards below South America, so earthquakes should (and indeed do) get deeper from west to east. [The destructive plate boundary B–B′ in Figure 2.4 is a mirror image of the one shown in TYVET Figure 2.6.]

Question 2.7

Volcanoes tend not to occur at conservative (transform fault) plate boundaries where one plate slides sideways against another (TYVET p. 19), because here there is no obvious cause of magma generation (TYVET p. 22).

Question 3.1

There are several ways of doing this. One is to turn the rate of erosion into millimetres per year: 1 cm per century is 10 mm per century. To turn this into millimetres per year, divide by 100, arriving at (10/100) mm per year, which is 1/10 mm per year. Scientifically this is expressed as 10^{-1} mm per year, in which 10^{-1} means 1/10 or 0.1. (If you have not met this concept before, see Section 7.2 of the Maths Skills ebook.) To calculate how long it would take to erode away 10 km at this rate, 10 km must be expressed in millimetres and then this number is divided by the rate of erosion in mm per year. Now, 10 km is 10^{7} mm (because there are 10^{6} mm in 1 km), so the time taken for erosion is (10^{7} mm/10^{-1}) mm per year = $10^{7+1} = 10^{8}$ years, which is 100 million years.

[If this explanation is still a mystery to you, you should refer to the Maths Skills ebook for help. Handling large and small numbers, and working things out numerically, are skills that every scientist needs to an extent. Mathematics is not a large part of this course, and you will be able to pass even if you ignore the numerical aspects. However, if you want to go further in science, it will not be so easy to do that.]

Question 3.2

TYVET describes the processes in the following order:

Mixing with other batches of magma Each batch may have a different composition at first and mixing may be complete (so the mixed batch has a uniform composition that is an average of the starting batches) or incomplete (so the combined batch is patchy in composition).

Assimilation Lumps of rock are engulfed as the magma rises and (if their melting temperature is lower than the magma's) can melt and mix in with the magma. This will increase the silica content of the magma.

Fractional crystallisation Crystals form within the magma, and crystals and melt become separated. The crystals that form first are poorer in silica than the overall magma, so the melt becomes richer in silica than the original magma.

Degassing Volatile substances such as water, carbon dioxide and sulfur dioxide bubble out from the magma and escape.

Question 3.3

TYVET Table 3.1 shows that a VEI 8 erupted volume is more than 10^{12} m^3, which in plain English is 'more than ten to the twelve cubic metres' or 'more than one thousand billion cubic metres'. [A billion is one thousand million (10^9), so 10^{12} is one thousand billion.]

Question 3.4

TYVET Table 3.1 shows that, up to VEI 5, the greater the volume of erupted material, the higher the eruption column. For a VEI greater than 5, there is no such relationship, so clearly other factors must be in play. These include the speed of the blast at the vent (the force of the 'gas thrust' region) and the temperature profile of the atmosphere (which will determine the height of neutral buoyancy where the plume will spread out). These are both noted on TYVET p. 47. [The former varies with each volcano, the latter is controlled more strongly by latitude (columns tend to reach highest in the tropics) and by the altitude of the volcano's summit. A VEI 8 eruption tends to continue much longer than a VEI 5 eruption, sustaining an eruption column at a similar height for longer, rather than creating a much higher column.]

Question 3.5

You are told in the video that fissure eruptions are fed by dykes, usually feeding magma laterally from a volcano (rather than directly upwards). Magma can reach the surface either along the whole length of a dyke extending to the surface, or through feeder pipes that project upwards from a dyke whose top is at a shallow depth below the surface.

Question 3.6

(a) TYVET p. 62 states that there are 'about ten' VEI 6 eruptions every 1000 years. This must mean that there is about one VEI 6 eruption every 100 years. However, this is a long-term average, and it would not be surprising for some centuries to experience two or three such eruptions and for other centuries to have none.

(b) The same sentence in TYVET says there is 'only about one VEI 7 eruption' every 1000 years (although, of course, they don't happen like clockwork at 1000-year intervals). As for the likelihood of a VEI 7 eruption happening in your lifetime, it is best to keep the maths simple by assuming that you will live for a further 50 years. One VEI 7 eruption per 1000 years means that the chance of such a eruption in any particular year is 1/1000. The chance of a VEI 7 eruption during the remaining 50 years of your life is thus $50 \times (1/1000) = 50/1000 = 5/100$. You can also express this as 1/20 (a 'one in twenty') chance or a 5% chance.

Question 3.7

According to TYVET p. 29, dissolved water (identified on TYVET p. 35 as a volatile) reduces the viscosity of magma. The effect is greatest for high-viscosity (high-silica) magma, and less for low-viscosity (low-silica) magma. [Other volatiles also reduce viscosity.]

Question 3.8

As described on TYVET p. 52, and illustrated in Plate 7 and in the 'Lava flows' video (Activity 3.1), the edge of a lava dome (which is an effusive feature) on a steep slope (or of a steep-sided lava dome irrespective of slope) can collapse, generating a mixture of ash particles and blocks of rock that can sweep downhill as the variety of pyroclastic flow described as a 'block and ash flow' or a 'nuée ardente'.

Question 3.9

Carbonatite is a non-silicate type of magma (TYVET p. 28) and has the lowest viscosity of all. The others are varieties of silicate magma, and, in order of increasing silica content, and hence viscosity, they are basalt, andesite, rhyolite. The full list in order of increasing viscosity is thus: carbonatite, basalt, andesite, rhyolite.

Question 3.10

(a) Both types are powerful, explosive pyroclastic eruptions, producing eruption columns and umbrella clouds from which bombs and finer-grained material fall (airfall). Both are powered by the violent escape of gas brought near to the surface in a magma conduit.

(b) In a plinian eruption the fragmented material consists mostly of fresh magma, whereas in a vulcanian eruption it consists mostly of pre-existing rock that had choked the upper part of the conduit. The largest plinian eruptions are bigger than the largest vulcanian eruptions.

Question 3.11

Eruption under water can chill the skin of the lava so rapidly that it forms pillow lava (for example, TYVET Figure 3.27), which forms *only* under water. On land (or at progressively higher rates of flow under water) basalt lava takes the form of pahoehoe at slow flow rates and a'a at higher flow rates. In pahoehoe the lava flows beneath a flexible skin, and in a'a the surface of the moving flow is continually ruptured into jagged blocks (both are shown in Figure 3.6).

Question 3.12

The only correct statements are as follows.

1. Volcanic eruptions always trigger volcanogenic earthquakes.
2. Tectonic earthquakes sometimes trigger volcanic eruptions.
3. Volcanic eruptions never trigger tectonic earthquakes.
4. Volcanogenic earthquakes never trigger volcanic eruptions.

[With regard to 4: volcanogenic earthquakes indicating underground magma movement are often *precursors* to an eruption, but it is unlikely that they act as independent *triggers* for an eruption.]

Question 4.1

They have all experienced collapse of one or more of their flanks, producing debris avalanche deposits (which are submarine in the case of Tenerife and the Hawaiian Islands).

Question 4.2

Basalt has a lower viscosity than the magmas typically erupted to form composite cone volcanoes. Therefore, it flows freely away from the vent, spreading out over a wide area. Composite cone volcanoes form mainly from andesitic magma, so lava flows are relatively viscous and do not travel as far as basalt. (However, the shape of the volcano is also controlled by ash from explosive eruptions, which are more common in composite cone volcanoes too.)

Question 4.3

Eruption of a scoria cone involves least water; the volatiles causing the explosive eruption are gases brought up with the magma. However, in eruptions that produce both tuff cones and tuff rings, the magma mixes with water (groundwater, or a shallow sea or lake). As explained on TYVET p. 89, the steam-to-magma ratio is higher for tuff cones. The correct order of increasing water content is thus: scoria cone, tuff ring, tuff cone.

Question 4.4

'Volcano' is not a straightforward term to define. You may have noticed the TYVET Glossary definition – 'a landscape feature at a site where magma is erupted'. If you identified that, or something like it, you probably have as good a short definition as it is possible to get. If you wrote 'a mountain where magma is erupted' (as you could be excused for doing *before* you read the chapter), you would be wrong, because neither calderas nor the sources of flood basalts are adequately described as 'mountains'. Also, depending on how you define 'mountain,' such a definition may exclude submarine volcanoes too. Many definitions that you can find by searching the internet fall into those traps. As an example of further complication, TYVET p. 66 discusses the pitfalls of deciding whether neighbouring vents are separate volcanoes or parts of a single volcano.

Question 5.1

1. The data in the table are incomplete or unreliable for many parts of the globe, especially in the first half of the 400-year period considered.
2. Few eruptions of VEI 7 and above occurred in that period. A single such eruption could change the balance completely.
3. Population growth is continuing to put more people at risk [and, indeed, to change the nature of the risk, as you will see in Chapter 8].

Question 5.2

You would prefer to see a lava flow because pyroclastic flows travel much faster than lava flows (about 100 km per hour), whereas most lava flows barely exceed walking pace (although the exceptional Nyiragongo flow in 1977 moved at 30 km per hour). So, provided you are alert and able, you could get out of the way of a lava flow (unless escape routes are blocked), whereas you would be much less likely to evade a pyroclastic flow.

Question 5.3

A pyroclastic flow can be initiated by:

1. dome collapse, e.g. Mount Pelée in 1902 (also Unzen in 1991, Soufriere Hills, Montserrat in 1997 and many others)
2. directed blast, e.g. Mount St Helens in 1980
3. column collapse, e.g. Mount Pinatubo in 1991 (also El Chichón in 1982, Vesuvius in AD 79, and many others).

[These methods of starting a pyroclastic flow are described in Chapter 3.]

Question 5.4

The weight of an airfall deposit can cause roofs to collapse, so it is sensible to sweep them clean during an eruption. Large bombs can cause damage by the speed of their impact so, if you are caught in the open while bombs are falling, it is safer to watch the bombs and dodge them when necessary rather than turning and running. Fine ash can cause respiratory problems, so try to avoid stirring it up and wear a face mask. Vehicles can be ruined if ash gets into the engine or lubrication systems, or if the engine overheats because the radiator is clogged by ash, so drive slowly or not at all.

Question 5.5

A lahar can begin during an eruption if it causes snow or ice to melt, as happened at Nevado del Ruiz in 1985. [You could also have suggested Ruapehu in 1953 or Mount St Helens in 1980.] A lahar can happen after an eruption when heavy rain falls on airfall ash deposits, such as after the eruption of Mount Pinatubo in 1991. [You could also have suggested heavy rainfall on weak, fumarolically altered rock, as on Casita volcano in 1998.]

Question 6.1

According to the narrator, the climate effect depends on how large the aerosol particles are and how long they remain in suspension (in the atmosphere).

Question 6.2

Sigurdsson said that the fluorine gas is 'adsorbed' onto ash. The ash falls to the ground, contaminates vegetation and is then ingested by grazing animals, causing 'fluorosis' and diseases including gout and loss of teeth. ['Adsorbed' means almost the same as 'absorbed', except that it refers to sticking to the *surface* of the ash, rather than soaking into the ash. Fluorosis is a disease caused by excess fluorine in drinking water or diet, of which the chief symptom is abnormal bone growth, notably affecting the joints.]

Question 6.3

In TYVET Table 4.1 the smallest recorded flood basalt volume is 0.2 million cubic kilometres, for the Columbia River flood basalts. To compare the two values, divide one by the other, thus: (15 km^3)/(0.2 million km^3). Now, 'km^3' appears in both parts, so it cancels out, leaving a simple ratio 15/(0.2 million), which is 15/200 000. If you have a calculator handy, it will show you that this is equal to 7.5×10^{-5}. In other words, the Laki fissure eruption erupted only a tiny fraction of the total amount erupted to form the Colombia River flood basalt province; however, you should bear in mind that the latter required numerous eruptions spaced over maybe half a million years, whereas the Laki eruption lasted only 8 months. [The value of 0.2 million km^3 in the table is just a crude approximation so, rather than quoting your result to two significant figures, it would be more realistic to round it to 8×10^{-5} or even call it 'about 10^{-4}'. Examples quoting 'significant figures' scarcely feature in this course, but you should refer to Section 9 in the Maths Skills ebook if you want to know more about this issue.]

Question 6.4

El Chichón is at 17.36° N and Pinatubo is at 15.13° N. Thus, Pinatubo is slightly closer to the Equator than El Chichón. The first paragraph of TYVET Chapter 6 states: 'If the eruption is near the Equator, both hemispheres can be affected.' It is possible that El Chichón was a little too far north for its plume to penetrate into the atmospheric circulation system of the Southern Hemisphere, even though the difference in latitude amounts to about only 220 km. Another factor that would help the plume from Pinatubo to spread is that Pinatubo expelled twice as much sulfur dioxide as El Chichón (20 million as opposed to 10 million tonnes). [The local wind direction during the eruption would also play a part. If a plume is blown towards the Equator, it can more easily spread into the opposite hemisphere than if it is blown away from the Equator.]

Question 6.5

According to TYVET Table 3.1, VEI 6 eruptions eject between 10^{10} m^3 and 10^{11} m^3. To compare this with the '30 cubic kilometres' attributed to the Taupo eruption, cubic kilometres must be converted to cubic metres (this is signified by 'm^3'). There are 1000 (which is 10^3) metres in a kilometre, so 30 cubic kilometres is:

$$30 \times 10^3 \text{ m} \times 10^3 \text{ m} \times 10^3 \text{ m} = 30 \times 10^{3+3+3} \text{ m} \times \text{m} \times \text{m} = 30 \times 10^9 \text{ m}^3$$
$$= 3.0 \times 10^{10} \text{ m}^3.$$

This value is clearly more than 10^{10} m^3 but less than 10^{11} m^3, so it does lie within the range of volumes given for VEI 6 eruptions.

Question 6.6

There is no 'right' answer, but this question should have made you think. You may decide to do nothing, on the grounds that a supervolcanic eruption is so unlikely to occur during your lifetime, or even during that of your grandchildren, that it is not worth worrying about. (This is essentially the attitude of most governments, although some recognise the need for more research to understand the threat more clearly.) You may decide to stockpile vast amounts of food against this unlikely eventuality. (Can you afford this? Will you have enough to share, or are you prepared to fight off starving people?) If your country is near a potential supervolcano, you may decide to build bunkers for shelter. You could even decide that the risk of civilisation being unable to survive the trauma of a supervolcanic eruption makes it imperative to establish self-sufficient colonies of humans elsewhere in the Solar System. You may take a fatalistic approach, recognising that such an eruption is bound to happen eventually, and that the survivors will just have to find a way to cope.

Question 7.1

As explained at the start of TYVET Chapter 7, a large volcanic eruption is usually preceded by smaller eruptions, and heralded by other warning signs (such as seismic activity), whereas a major tectonic earthquake is likely to strike without warning and be followed by smaller 'aftershocks'.

Question 7.2

You may have used different words but you should have written down the causes in Table 7.2.

Table 7.2 Causes of volcanogenic earthquakes.

Type	Cause
high-frequency event	Episodes of rock fracture and/or fault movement
low-frequency event	Episodes of magma or gas migration
volcanic tremor	Sustained magma or gas migration
very long period event	Probably high-pressure gas movements

Question 7.3

RSAM stands for Real-time Seismic Amplitude Measurement. It is useful because, when there are too many seismic events for scientists to inspect, a computer can calculate RSAM, which is a better guide to the intensity of activity than simply counting the number of earthquakes.

Question 7.4

An increase in gravity *can* indicate the arrival of magma (or the replacement of bubbly magma with bubble-free magma), but it can also indicate subsidence (bringing the gravity station closer to the Earth's centre).

Question 7.5

The Yellowstone caldera *inflated* by 18 cm at its centre between 1976 and 1984, then it *deflated* by 14 cm between 1985 and 1992, and then *inflated* by 16 cm between 1992 and 2003. Additional data to support the assertion of magma movement would include microgravity data (to tell whether the mass below the caldera was changing in pace with the inflation–deflation) and seismic data (especially low-frequency events denoting magma movement at an appropriate depth).

Question 8.1

The list below was compiled from TYVET Chapter 5, but excludes ash clouds affecting aircraft in flight because 'airfall' really means debris that has fallen to the ground.

- Impact damage (by large bombs) to property and people
- Roof collapse because of accumulated weight
- Leaves stripped from vegetation
- Respiratory problems (both during airfall and if stirred up again)
- Damage to engines and other machinery
- Liability to turn into a lahar when rain falls on it

Sometimes it is convenient to regard each of these as a separate hazard, particularly because the ways to reduce vulnerability, and thereby reduce the risk posed by the hazard, differ in several cases.

Question 8.2

(a) There are no towns shown on the map in the areas at risk from lahars at recurrence intervals of less than 100 years.

(b) Two settlements are clearly within areas with a lahar recurrence interval of 100–500 years: Packwood (to the south) and Greenwater (to the north), but also the whole of the larger towns of Orting and Sumner, much of Puyallup and a significant part of Tacoma.

(c) Additional towns at risk from lahars approximately every 500–1000 years are: in the south, Randle (part of which may lie within the 100–500 year zone), Elbe (just beyond the terminus of the 100–500 year zone on the Nisqually River), Ashford, Carbonado, Wilkeson, Auburn, and small extra areas of Tacoma and Puyallup.

Question 8.3

My version is given in Table 8.1. You may have picked on some other items to include. My table greatly simplifies two rather complex series of events, and is perhaps somewhat unfair to the people who made mistakes.

Table 8.1 Sample answer to Question 8.3.

	Soufrière in 1976	**Nevado del Ruiz in 1985**
(a) Scientific advice	Contradictory views from rival teams, which were sometimes wrong	No evidence of rivalry between teams. Consistent advice
(b) Government action	Rapid evacuation ordered on basis of mistaken identification of fresh magma evidence. A 'panic measure'	Did not act on warnings from scientists (and ignored two historic precedents). Told inhabitants to stay in their homes
(c) Fate of inhabitants	Evacuated unnecessarily for several months. Economic losses	Majority killed, survivors homeless

Question 8.4

A dome was growing within the summit crater, so a collapse of the dome or another part of the volcano leading to such events as pyroclastic flows, a directed blast, or a debris avalanche was unlikely. However, a build-up of gas or gas-rich fresh magma in the conduit could have caused a major explosive eruption of the plinian type. The worst outcomes would therefore have been column collapse feeding pyroclastic flows and/or a large volume of airfall. In the end, explosions were relatively small, and did not produce a high, sustained column [the VAAS in TYVET Chapter 5 reports the highest ash to be between 30 000 and 35 000 feet, which is about 10 km above sea level, and the GVP report mentions the ash plume 'more than 8 km above the summit crater' on 22 January, which is about 14 km above sea level]. In addition, melting of the summit ice could lead to lahars [the GVP report mentions one reaching 15 km in February].

Question 9.1

The bed of sandstone at the place where the woman is standing has been moved down (by about 1 m) relative to the same bed on the left of the fault. The shaley, brown unit below the sandstone is clearly exposed on both sides of the fault and, of course, is displaced by the same amount. The fault is inclined steeply down from left to right and, because the beds have been moved down on the right, movement on this fault was associated with local extension and is therefore what geologists call a 'normal' fault. The situation is the same as shown in TYVET Figure 9.4c.

Question 9.2

Shallow earthquakes can be more powerful (have a greater magnitude) because the greater strength of rock near the surface allows more strain to build up before rupture occurs. The focus of a deep earthquake is further away from the surface so, even for equal magnitude quakes, the intensity at the epicentre will be less than for a deep quake (the further away, the less powerful the shaking). [An additional factor is that deep earthquakes are too deep to generate surface waves (which are the most damaging sort) directly. Surface waves in such a case can form only by interaction between body waves and the ground surface, and will be weaker than if formed at the rupture itself.]

Question 9.3

The answer is given at the start of the section 'Prediction and warning': most volcanic eruptions build up towards a crescendo, but only 10% of large earthquakes are preceded by foreshocks (and even those can be mistaken for the main quake rather than foreshocks heralding something bigger).

Question 9.4

Prediction is when the time and/or nature of a future earthquake is forecast, whereas a warning is issued during the brief time interval after an event has begun but before it is has caused damage. Earthquake warning works because P-waves (which tend not to cause damage) travel faster than the more violent surface waves. Question 9.5 involves a simple calculation relevant to this.

Question 9.5

(a) To find the time taken to travel 200 km at 6.0 km/s, simply divide the distance by the speed:

$$\frac{200\text{km}}{6.0\text{km/s}} = 33\text{s}.$$

So P-waves will take 33s to arrive.

(b) Similarly, at a speed of 3.5 km/s the time taken is:

$$\frac{200\text{km}}{3.5\text{km/s}} = 57\text{s}.$$

The difference between the two is 57s – 33s = 24s. This is less than half a minute's warning, which is far too little to enable evacuation. However, as

TYVET explains, it is long enough to enact safety precautions (such as setting traffic lights to red, stopping lifts and cutting power to trains). [Note that a warning transmitted electronically from a seismometer that was closer to the epicentre than your town could give almost a minute's warning even for an earthquake only 200 km away.]

Question 9.6

'First arrival' refers to the P-waves. The onset of the P-waves is marked by an upward deflection in the seismogram shown in TYVET Figure 9.7, which represents upward ground movement. As explained in Box 9.1, upward movement happens during the arrival of a compressional manifestation of a P-wave, so the first arrival in this example is compressional.

Question 10.1

You must make your own judgement about this. In the 20th century, at least one million people were killed by earthquakes and, in round numbers, about 100 000 by volcanoes (you can deduce approximate figures like this from TYVET Tables 5.1 and 10.1). So, for the 20th century, earthquakes were 'worse'.

However, a more general answer must depend on how long a timescale you want to consider: do you bother about supervolcanic eruptions that happen globally only about once every 50 000 years? There was no such eruption during the 20th century, but there were numerous earthquakes of M8 or above (one per year expected according to TYVET Table 9.1), and it is reasonable to regard the 20th century as fairly average, while recognising that occasionally the death toll will be increased by an M9 earthquake in a major city. Offsetting that against future improvements in earthquake proofing and preparedness, for the sake of argument, the long-term death toll from earthquakes can be regarded as about one million per century.

Turning now to supervolcanoes, the estimate of one every 50 000 years means that the chance of one occurring in any given century is 1 in 500. If a supervolcanic eruption were to cause one billion deaths, the death rate per century works out as (1 billion)/500 = 2 million. On that basis, supervolcanoes *alone* are a 'worse' threat than earthquakes, and that is without factoring in the 100 000 deaths per century from 'ordinary' eruptions. However, if the 'average' supervolcanic eruption kills 'only' 100 million rather than one billion, the death rate is reduced to 200 000 per century, which is fewer than the earthquake deaths.

In summary, there is no clear answer. You may reach a different conclusion, but you should have considered the factors alluded to here. Scientists do not know for sure how many people a supervolcanic eruption is likely to kill, or the knock-on effects of such an eruption. (Would a catastrophe of that magnitude destroy world order and civilisation?)

Question 10.2

This building was damaged by the 1985 Mexico City earthquake. Eleven stories survive in the damaged wing, and between one and three top stories have collapsed (the walls gave way, and the roof and intervening floors squashed down on those below). The building was thus in the 5–20 stories height range which suffered from resonant amplification of the ground motion within the building structure.

Question 10.3

There are many ways, including: tying roofs to walls; tying walls to foundations; making deep foundations on bedrock (where motion is less than in soil); bracing to withstand twisting motions; fitting seismic shock absorbers.

Question 10.4

According to the advice from the Los Angeles telephone directory reproduced on TYVET pp. 254–5, which is repeated in a similar form in many other places: get underneath a table (to protect yourself – particularly your head – from falling objects), hold on to it, and be prepared to move with the table if it is shaken around.

Question 10.5

The high-hazard zone on the Atlantic coast is centred on Charleston, South Carolina, where there was a powerful intra-plate earthquake in 1886 (not shown in Figure 10.4a) and the inland zone picks out the 1811 New Madrid, Missouri earthquake and its aftershocks in 1812. It is possible that the map overestimates the hazard in these two areas: for example, because of overestimating the likely frequency of earthquakes there in step (d) of Figure 10.4.

Question 11.1

The Pacific Ocean is almost entirely ringed by subduction zones ('destructive' or 'convergent' plate boundaries) where big earthquakes can occur with epicentres on the sea floor. The Indian Ocean has only one subduction zone (where the earthquakes occurred that caused the tsunamis in 2004 and 2006 in Java). The Atlantic Ocean has only two short lengths of subduction zone (below the Caribbean and Scotia arcs), although the only Atlantic tsunami described in TYVET was the result of a submarine landslip (rather than of the fault motion itself) triggered by an intra-plate earthquake.

Question 11.2

A wave trough rather than a wave crest could be the first manifestation of a group of tsunami waves to arrive, or fault motion could have moved this part of the land upwards relative to sea level.

Question 11.3

1. A seismogenic tsunami results from the sudden displacement of seawater because of a shallow submarine earthquake.
2. A landslide tsunami is caused by the sudden displacement of seawater by a landslide (which can be entirely submarine, or can enter the sea from dry land).
3. An impact tsunami is the result of a comet or an asteroid striking the ocean.
4. A volcanogenic tsunami is the result of a volcanic eruption.

[In the case of volcanic collapse or a pyroclastic flow hitting the sea, this is effectively the same mechanism as a landslide tsunami; the submarine collapse of a caldera is similar to the way a seismogenic tsunami is triggered; but an underwater volcanic explosion is an entirely different mechanism.]

Question 11.4

The first sign of the tsunami is an upward deflection of the trace (shortly before 14.00 GMT), representing an increase of about 0.08 m (8 cm) in the water height above the pressure sensor, so this was a wave crest rather than a trough. However, the tsunami waves are superimposed on a longer period tidal curve, which was still going down when the first wave arrived, although the tide was on the rise again by the time four major tsunami wave troughs had passed.

Question 11.5

As stated in TYVET, for an impact to cause a powerful tsunami, the diameter of the transient crater in the sea surface must be at least three times the water depth. Transient craters are about 20 times the diameter of the impactor that causes them, so the transient crater produced by a 200 m impactor would be about 4 km (20×200 m = 4000 m = 4 km) across. This is *less than* three times the depth of the Atlantic Ocean but *more than* three times the depth of the North Sea. Thus, of these two equal, 200 m-wide fragments, the one striking the Atlantic would probably not cause a powerful tsunami, but the one hitting the North Sea would. An additional factor is that the North Sea is much more closely confined by coasts, so any waves generated would not lose much of their strength, whereas the Atlantic is much bigger, so wave power would be reduced by the time any waves reached a coastline.

Discussion of activities

Activity 1.1

In learning about volcanoes, you will discover that eruptions are usually associated with small earthquakes, and that in some circumstances the eruption of a volcano can displace seawater and cause a tsunami. For example, most of the fatalities attributed to the famous 1883 eruption of Krakatau (popularly referred to as Krakatoa) were caused by the associated tsunami. You will also discover that it is not just the people living close to a volcano who are at risk from volcanic activity. In addition to generating an ocean-crossing tsunami, a volcanic eruption can reach up and pluck aircraft from the sky. Worse, the most violent eruptions, of a kind that happen on average about once in 50,000 years, can cause global famine and ecosystem collapse by blotting out the Sun for months on end. Therefore, this book also considers the interactions between volcanoes, on the one hand, and the environment and climate, on the other.

Later in the book the focus shifts to tectonic earthquakes. These are earthquakes that involve rupture and slippage of the Earth's crust, as a result of the internal mobility of the Earth rather than being directly associated with volcanic activity. In contrast to volcanoes, no earthquake is likely to be capable of causing devastation on a global or continent-wide scale. However, the largest examples can cause much more violent shaking of the surface than occurs during a volcanic eruption and, during the twentieth century, earthquakes claimed many more lives than volcanic eruptions. Several of the world's great cities are in regions prone to earthquakes (San Francisco, Los Angeles, Istanbul, Tokyo ...), the rural populations of many mountain belts are at risk too, as shown by the 8 October 2005 Muzaffarabad (Kashmir) earthquake that claimed over 80,000 lives, and coastal communities can suffer dreadfully from tsunamis triggered by submarine earthquakes. Here, you will find out about earthquake prediction, and the measures that can be taken to limit the damage caused by earthquakes.

Finally I will discuss tsunamis in their own right, including those triggered by means other than volcanic eruptions and earthquakes, the most frightening being a tsunami caused by the impact of a comet or asteroid into the ocean. This is a dangerous planet that we live on, but (for the time being) it is the only one that we have!

Figure 1.3 Example of highlighting key parts of the text on TYVET pp. 3–4.

Figure 1.3 shows an example of highlighting important words and phrases in the fourth, fifth and sixth paragraphs of TYVET Chapter 1. There are other ways of doing this, and it would be very surprising if your highlighting exactly matches this. Remember that your highlighting is for *your* benefit so, provided you are satisfied that you have picked out things that will be helpful for *you*, you don't need to match these specific suggestions. At this early stage, one valid approach is to highlight topics you would like to know more about as you study the rest of the book.

In the fourth paragraph of Chapter 1, the important points are: (i) volcanic eruptions are usually associated with small earthquakes, and an eruption can also cause a tsunami, and (ii) the most violent eruptions can affect the entire globe. This is highlighted accordingly, including an indication of how often the latter occur.

In the fifth paragraph, *tectonic earthquakes* and the words that seem to explain what was meant by this term are highlighted. Phrases were picked out showing that the effects of a single earthquake are more localised than the effects of eruptions (although in the last century more people were killed by earthquakes), and examples of places at risk from earthquakes.

In the sixth paragraph, the causes listed for tsunamis are highlighted.

As you continue to highlight text throughout TYVET, your aim should be to do it in a way that, when you return to that page in future, you will immediately be drawn to the crucial bits. Even if you never look at that page again, the decisions you make while highlighting will help you understand and remember the main points that the text is trying to tell you.

Activity 2.1

Figure 2.9 shows an example of highlighting the text. In the first two paragraphs the main characteristics of a constructive plate boundary are picked out. In the next two paragraphs the highlighting is intended to drawn attention to why melting occurs in this setting, and the nature of the compositional changes. If your intention was the same, your highlighting should be similar (although it won't be identical). However, it's fine if you decided that other sorts of information will be more useful to you, provided that you are still happy with it.

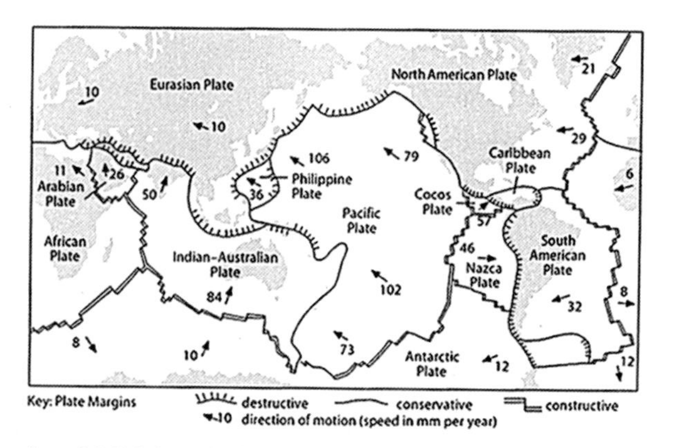

figure 2.4 Global map showing plate boundaries and the rates of plate motion (expressed relative to Africa, which is almost stationary). The three types of plate boundary are discussed in the text.

Plates moving apart

First, what happens when plates are moving apart? This tends to occur mostly within the oceans, at sites known as constructive plate boundaries. What goes on here is summarised in figure 2.5.

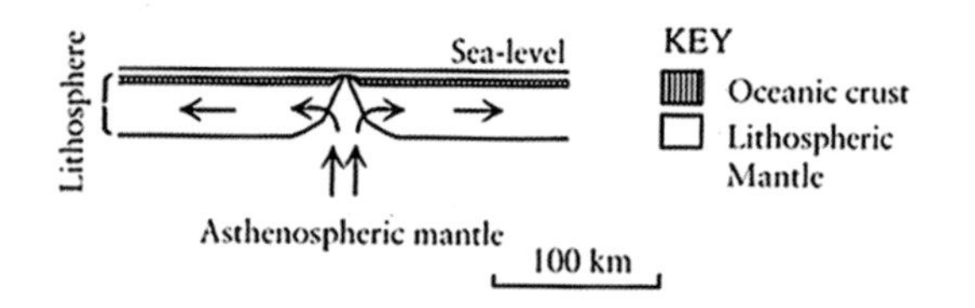

figure 2.5 Cross-section through a constructive plate boundary, where upwelling asthenosphere accretes to the diverging edges of two lithospheric plates. The oceanic crust is produced by partial melting that occurs during upwelling of the asthenospheric mantle. See text for explanation.

As two oceanic plates are drawn apart, in a process referred to as sea-floor spreading, the underlying asthenosphere wells upwards to avoid any gaps appearing. The upwelling asthenospheric mantle cools as it nears the surface and becomes rigid enough to join the lithosphere belonging to the plates on either side of the plate boundary. This new lithosphere is still relatively warm, which makes it slightly less dense and therefore more buoyant than the older, colder lithosphere further from the boundary, so constructive plate boundaries are marked by broad ridges on the ocean floor. Typically, the crest of such a ridge lies at a depth of 2–3 km below sea-level, whereas the expanse of ocean floor to either side is at an average depth of 4–5 km. The rifting and subsidence associated with the stretching apart of new lithosphere produces characteristic earthquakes at shallow depths (typically about 10 km) below the ridge crest.

During the upwelling of the mantle below a constructive plate boundary, as each bit in turn arrives within about 100 km of the surface a small percentage of it melts. This is not because there is a heat source here, but is a consequence of the drop in pressure, that leads to melt generation by a process known as decompression melting. When mantle of peridotite composition (about 45 per cent silica, SiO_2) begins to melt (whether because of a drop in pressure as in this case, or for some other reason), the liquid sweated out from it has a slightly higher silica content. Magma produced in this way approaches the surface and solidifies to form the oceanic crust, the composition of which is, on average, about 49 per cent silica. This composition is described as basaltic, because it matches the composition of the rock type known as basalt (defined as containing 45–52 per cent silica). The residual mantle left behind has a reduced silica content to compensate for the enrichment of silica in the magma that was extracted from it. However, because the volume of magma produced is very much smaller than the volume of mantle contributing to the melt, the resulting chemical change in the mantle is slight.

The melting of a large volume of rock to yield a smaller volume of melt enriched in silica (and certain other components) is a very important process in geology, and is known as partial melting. The whole of the oceanic crust has been produced by partial melting of the mantle. We will look in more detail at the sub-sea volcanism associated with constructive plate boundaries and the origin of the oceanic crust in Chapter 04.

Plates colliding

Averaged out round the globe, the rate of creation of oceanic lithosphere at constructive plate boundaries is balanced by the rate at which old ocean floor is being destroyed at sites known

Figure 2.9 Example of highlighting key parts of the text on TYVET pp. 14–15.

For a discussion of all the other activities, please see the Study Guide.

Acknowledgements

Grateful acknowledgement is made to the following sources:

Cover: *Behind the Great Wave at Kanagawa*, Japanese woodblock print (1832) by Katsushika Hokusai (1760–1849).

Figs. 1.2a & 6.3: Steve Blake; Figs. 1.2b–d, 3.2–3.8, 4.1, 4.2, 4.3b, 4.4, 4.8, 4.9, 4.11, 5.7, 6.10, 7.2, 7.8a, 7.9, 9.2, 11.7: David Rothery; Figs. 2.1 & 3.1: Andy Tindle; Fig. 2.5: adapted from the British Geological Survey World Seismicity Database. Global Seismology and Geomagnetism Group, Edinburgh; Fig. 2.6: from US National Intelligence Mapping Agency GTOPO30 digital elevation data, map designed by Steve Drury for the S339 course team; Fig. 2.7: Nick Rogers; Fig. 2.8: courtesy of Dr Pierre Wiart; Fig. 4.3a: courtesy of US Forest Service, Skamania County, Washington, United States Geological Survey; Fig. 4.5: The National Museum of Natural History, Global Volcanism Program, Photos by Lee Siebert © 2007 Smithsonian Institution; Fig. 4.6b: Mike Widdowson; Fig. 4.7b: Steve Self; Fig. 4.10: C. Nye on 9th May 1994, Alaska Division of Geological and Geophysical Survey, United States Geological Survey; Figs. 4.12a, 4.13 & 5.3: Peter Francis; Fig. 4.12b: courtesy of Dr John Smellie, British Antarctic Survey; Figs. 4.14a, 11.2, 11.4–11.6, 11.8, 11.9: courtesy of NOAA; Fig. 4.14b: © 2001 MBARI; Figs. 5.1 & 5.2: Hawaiian Volcano Observatory, United States Geological Survey; Fig. 5.4: Richard P. Hoblitt, photograph taken 12th June 1991, Cascades Volcano Observatory, United States Geological Survey; Fig. 5.5: USGS 1997, Modified from Tilling, Topinka and Swanson, 1990, Eruptions of Mount St Helens. Present and Future, USGS Special Interest Publication; Fig. 5.6: Ward, S. N, and Day, S. (2001), 'Cumbre Vieja Volcano – Potential collapse and tsunami at La Palma, Canary Islands' *Geophysical Research Letters*, 28(17) 2001, American Geophysical Union; Fig. 6.4: courtesy of Image Science & Analysis Laboratory, NASA; Fig. 6.5a: France (w/c on paper), Turner, Joseph Mallord William (1775–1851)/British Museum, London, UK,/The Bridgeman Art Library; Fig. 6.5b: Science Museum Pictorial/Science and Society Picture Library; Fig. 6.6: http://en.wikipedia.org/wiki/image:instrumental_temperature_record.pn; Figs. 6.7 & 6.8: NASA; Fig. 6.9: Adapted from Oppenheimer C., (2003) 'Ice core and palaeoclimatic evidence', *International Journal of Climatology*, 2003. Royal Meteorological Society;OU; Fig. 7.5: UNAVCO Inc; Fig. 7.6: Photographs taken by David Sherrod, United States Geological Survey; Fig. 7.7: J-L Fournier; Fig. 7.8b & 7.10: E. Marchetti; Fig. 7.11: J. Dehn; Fig. 7.12: Diego Coppola; Fig. 7.13: David Schneider, United States Geological Survey; Fig. 7.14: © 2004, University of Hawai'i; Fig. 7.15: Johnston Ridge Observatory, Mount St Helens National Volcanic Monument; Figs. 8.1–8.3, 9.5, 10.1a, 10.3–10.5: United States Geological Survey; Figs 10.1b & 10.2 FEMA picture library; Fig. 11.1: *The Guardian*; *The Independent*; Fig. 11.3: AusAId/Robin Davies.

Every effort has been made to contact copyright holders. If any have been inadvertently overlooked the publishers will be pleased to make the necessary arrangements at the first opportunity.

INDEX

Page numbers in *italics* refer to figures or tables